Wonders of the Earth

The geological world around us comes thrillingly alive in this unusual book. Compiled by Samuel Rapport and Helen Wright, who have collaborated on such books as *A Treasury of Science* and *Great Adventures in Medicine*, *The Crust of the Earth* gives you a wealth of fascinating facts about the history, composition, past, and future of the earth.

Here is an authoritative presentation of the most important theories concerning the birth of the earth and a clear explanation of how scientists determine its age, size, shape, internal structure, axial revolution, and movement in the solar system. You will discover how glaciers, seas, deserts, and mountains form, what makes volcanoes erupt and produce mineral deposits, how hurricanes and earthquakes unleash their fury.

Looking back through the ages, the various authors, all experts in their special fields, describe the spectacular variety of strange creatures that once lived on a very different earth. Peering into the future, they present a startling forecast of how our planet will be hundreds of thousands of years from now. . . .

Other SIGNET Science Library Books
60¢ each

The
Crust of the Earth

An Introduction to Geology

Edited by *SAMUEL RAPPORT*
and *HELEN WRIGHT*

A SIGNET SCIENCE LIBRARY BOOK
Published by THE NEW AMERICAN LIBRARY

ACKNOWLEDGMENTS AND COPYRIGHT NOTICES
*(The page following constitutes an extension of this
copyright page.)*

"Geology, the Easy Science" and "The Record of Living Things"
by William O. Hotchkiss, from *The Story of a Billion Years*,
Copyright 1932 by The Williams & Wilkins Company, reprinted
by permission of Nancy Hotchkiss Boschen.

"Second Rate Planet" and "Rocks and Minerals" by Carey
Croneis and William C. Krumbein from *Down to Earth*, Copyright
1936 by The University of Chicago, published by The University
of Chicago Press and reprinted by their permission.

"Interpretations of Nature" by Arthur Holmes from *Principles
of Physical Geology*, Copyright 1945 The Ronald Press Company,
published by The Ronald Press Company (New York) and Thomas
Nelson & Sons Ltd. (Edinburgh), reprinted by permission of the
author and the publishers.

"The Atmospheric Pattern" from *Global Geography* by George
T. Renner and Associates, Copyright, 1944, by Thomas Y. Crowell
Company, published by Thomas Y. Crowell Company and reprinted
by their permission.

"Crumbling Rocks" by Raymond E. Janssen from *The Scientific
Monthly*, August, 1947, Copyright, 1947, by The American Association for the Advancement of Science, reprinted by permission of
the author and The American Association for the Advancement of
Science.

Library of Congress Catalog Card No. 55-11508

*SIGNET SCIENCE LIBRARY BOOKS are published by
The New American Library of World Literature, Inc.
501 Madison Avenue, New York 22, New York*

CONTENTS

PART ONE

The Nature of the Earth

AT EXACTLY NINE O'CLOCK on the morning of October 26, 4004 B.C., the earth was created, according to a calculation made by the Irish Archbishop Ussher in the mid-seventeenth century. A Hindu calculation, described by Professor Holmes in "The Age of the Earth," placed creation 1,972,949,048 years before the date of his article (A.D. 1947). These mythologies gave explanations of the method as well as the time of creation. This is something modern science is not yet prepared to do, although it has offered a number of interesting hypotheses.

In 1796 the French scientist Laplace suggested that the solar system had originally been a diffuse gaseous nebula, hot and rotating. As the nebula cooled it shrank, leaving behind a series of rings which condensed into the planets and their satellites. The sun remained as residue. The ring which was the forerunner of the earth cooled gradually after condensing, in time became liquid, then solid. This hypothesis gained widespread popularity, but now, as the result of further calculation, it has been abandoned.

Early in the present century the Americans Chamberlin and Moulton suggested that the partial disruption of the sun occurred several billion years ago because of huge tides raised by the close approach of another star. A large amount of matter was thrown off. Most of the ejected matter fell back into the sun, but the rest coalesced into small fragments or planetesimals. After a long period of time, perhaps twenty million years, the larger planetesimals gathered up the smaller to form the planets moving elliptically around the sun. This theory is known as the Planetesimal Hypothesis. Various modifications of it, including the Tidal Hypothesis of the Englishmen Jeans and Jeffreys, have been offered. Mathematical calculations about the possibility of another star approaching near enough to the sun to cause the necessary gravitational pull indicate that while the chance does exist, it is exceedingly remote. It seems more likely, according to modern knowledge of the planets, that the solar system was born as a result of condensation. At the present time there is no theory on which astronomers, physicists, geologists and mathematicians can agree.

Whatever the method of creation, there is no doubt that the resultant globe is, to paraphrase, a second-rate planet revolving around a third-rate star. Far from being the center of the universe, the earth is of infinitesimal importance in the heavens. But it is our home and its study is of great importance to us as human beings. This study is known as geology. What it consists of and something of how it was founded and developed is explained in our first selection, "Geology, the Easy Science," by W. D. Hotchkiss, formerly State Geologist of Wisconsin, more recently President of Rensselaer Polytechnic Institute. His seemingly simple descriptions and comparisons lead us into a subject of great complexity. His account of the inspired guess of the Scotch farmer Hutton is the first chapter of a still little understood mystery, whose solution is taxing some of the best contemporary scientific brains.

The first and fundamental step in earth science is a determination of the earth's size, shape, mass, motion and distance from the sun. The basic methods for making these determinations are relatively simple. President Carey Croneis of Beloit College and Professor William C. Krumbein, now of Northwestern University, explain them with diagrams in "Second Rate Planet." Their short paper draws on the speculations of ancient philosophers and on the calculations of modern scientists.

Arthur Holmes, Regius Professor of Geology at the University of Edinburgh, next brings us to grips with the substance of physical geology in "Interpretations of Nature." In outline form he explains the great problems which earth science faces, the facts it has discovered and the direction it is taking. Here we learn something about the surface relief of the earth, its rocks, the great earth rhythms and their possible causes. The treatment is brief. Its purpose is to serve as an introduction to the more extended discussions which follow in later sections.

Geology, The Easy Science

By W. O. Hotchkiss

When the average intelligent person hears science mentioned, he thinks of it as something outside his daily affairs, something difficult, mysterious and even quite beyond his understanding. His impression is true only for the more advanced and specialized parts. It is not at all true for the great fundamental ideas and principles of science. These can be understood by the high-school graduate; they apply to the things with which he comes in daily contact.

In order to brush away the veil of mystery that too often surrounds science, we need to have these fundamental ideas and principles stated in familiar terms. We need to have explained to us, in words from our own vocabulary, that science is merely the statement of the orderly relations between facts, many of which each of us knows or can readily know from common-sense observations of the everyday things about us. Once this explanation is made, we are able to understand causes and effects, so that things begin to appear to us in delightfully simple and orderly relations and not as an appalling number of independent facts each of which must be separately mastered.

It is true that in geology, as in other sciences, there are mysteries and things difficult to understand. Fortunately these need not concern us greatly because most of the important facts are easily understood. All that need be done in order to give us a very satisfying knowledge of things geological is to call them to our attention. Geology concerns itself with the familiar hills and valleys, rivers and lakes, mountains and plains that surround us. It concerns itself not only with great wonders far away, but also with the small, intimate things we can see in our own neighborhood if our eyes are open.

One of the most enlightening things in the study of geology is the attainment of an adequate understanding of the vast time it has taken nature to write the record we see in the rocks. You and I live our lives in small units. When we were children, a quarter of an hour often seemed too long to be endured, particularly when we waited impatiently for the close of school or the start for a picnic. We measure our ordinary movements and the things close to us in feet and inches, in hours and minutes, in pounds and ounces. Because these units measure our daily activities and near surroundings, we have a fairly definite notion of what they mean. When we begin to group them into larger units and try to think in terms of miles and tons and years, our notions become less accurate. When we multiply these familiar units to describe a country, a mountain, or the life of a nation, the definiteness of our ideas fades and they become vague.

Among time units the longest we can understand from personal experience is our own life span. It is not surprising, then, that we can have no really accurate idea of so long a period as a century. If we think of the six or seven thousand years of recorded history, its beginnings seem incredibly far back, farther back than any of our familiar units will permit us to measure understandingly. When we try to imagine such a vast stretch of time as a billion years, the units we ordinarily use are so absurdly small that they afford us no useful comparison. We must resort to other comparisons to get any kind of picture at all. Let us imagine a man so small that he has to take sixteen steps to go one inch, and so slow that he can take but one step a year. If he lived in New York and wanted to walk to . . . Chicago he would have had to start a billion years ago.

In this story of the billion years of the existence of our earth, the tremendous length of the time involved is one of the ideas we find hard to grasp. Another is the number of things that can happen—even at a slow pace—in a billion years. At the rate of movement of our imaginary small man—one-sixteenth of an inch a year—a mountain range as high as the Rockies could be raised from sea level and lowered back to sea level one hundred and sixty times. A billion years has afforded time for the earth to go through many cycles of changes of great magnitude, and to do so in most leisurely manner. There has been time for the slow, unhurried development of the almost infinitely varied forms of vegetable and animal life. The days of creation have been long and well filled with labor. Well might the ancient Hebrew prophet say, "He stood, and measured the earth; . . . and the everlasting mountains were scattered, the perpetual hills did bow; his ways are everlasting." We can see the labors of creation continuing before our eyes, if we can but enlarge our mental time scale to permit us to see present events in their true relation to those of long ago.

The Story of a Wisconsin Millpond

Geology, in its efforts to bring this long time and its multitude of happenings into understandable scale, has found the year and the century too short to use as time units. It has grouped the past into larger units—into great cycles of similar events—so that our minds can picture them more readily.

To show you how these large group units are selected, I want to tell you the story of a Wisconsin millpond that I once studied for a few interesting hours. This pocket edition of a geologic epoch began with an unusual event in the history of a stream—the building of a dam. It was ended by another unusual event—a flood that destroyed the dam, and cut a tiny canyon through the sediments deposited in the pond. Such epochs, on a vastly larger time scale, measured by the deposition of hundreds or thousands of feet of sediments, are used as units in the story of the billion years of the history of the earth. They begin with an unusual event, the depression of a large area below sea level. They endure millions or tens of millions of years, during which events are infallibly recorded in the sediments. They end with another unusual event—the elevation of the area above the sea and its subjection to the action of the wind, of the rain and of the streams, which gradually wear it away.

As I looked at the vertical sides of the three-foot "canyon" cut in the sediments in the Wisconsin millpond, I could see the edges of thin horizontal layers of different kinds of mud. Closer examination showed that some of these layers were of coarse material and some of fine, that some were light colored and some dark. Some contained decayed leaves and other vegetable matter. By careful observation I could distinguish the layers that represented a year's deposit. Counting these annual layers told me that they had been accumulating for about seventy years. Information from neighboring farmers to the effect that the dam had been built seventy years before checked my observations most satisfactorily.

The alphabet of this story is simple. The little stream carried mud and sand, as all streams do. It carried fallen leaves in the autumn. It carried more mud and sand and more coarse material in flood times than in dry times. When it reached the still water of the pond, the sand and mud and even the leaves finally settled to the bottom, so that the water which escaped over the dam was much clearer than that which came into the pond. The coarser sand and small pebbles settled much more quickly than the fine mud.

With these simple, everyday facts as an alphabet I was prepared to read the story recorded in the mud layers behind the old dam. A thick layer of sand and fine pebbles told of a long past flood stage in the little stream. When, over that layer, I found a layer of the finest mud, I knew that the flood had subsided. A layer which contained leaves in fair abundance enabled me to deduce . . . that it must have been deposited in the autumn. When I found these leaf-bearing layers separated by thin layers of fine mud, I knew that there had come a period of dry years without heavy rainfall and floods; and when I found the leaf-bearing layers separated by thick beds of coarser-grained material, I was certain that they represented a period of years of heavy rainfall during which the stream was more often in flood. In this way I could identify both the dry years and the rainy years. If I had desired, I could have checked my conclusions by the local weather records. I could have checked them also by cutting a large tree nearby and observing the layers of annual growth. Wet years would have been represented by thick layers and dry years by thin. By a similar study of the annual rings of growth in the old trees of California and other places the weather records have been traced back beyond historical times. Thus, with satisfactory accuracy the climate of California in the time of Christ can be compared with that of the present.

DeGeer, studying the mud and sand deposits in ancient

Swedish lakes, found that the climate had left a continuous record for the last eight thousand years, so that it is possible to tell with quite pleasing accuracy the various "spells of weather" which marked that long stretch of time.

The story of the mud layers in the Wisconsin millpond illustrates perfectly three of the great fundamental principles of geology. The stream that flowed into the millpond was typical of all streams, big and little. It carried mud and sand and pebbles with it in its flow. It deposited this material when its rapid flow was stopped in the millpond. When the flood came that broke the dam, this deposit in the pond again started on its way toward the sea, to be redeposited in the next quiet water, and so by successive steps finally to be carried to the Gulf of Mexico and find a resting place in the sea.

The material carried into the millpond had been washed from the adjacent hillsides into the stream by the rain, a process called "erosion." Any sand bank or rivulet shows this process at work. It is the process which carved the magnificent gorge of the Grand Canyon, but it is not different from the process you can see going on in your back yard during a shower or when the garden hose is at work.

The other fundamental principles learned from the study of the millpond stream are known as "transportation" and "deposition." The stream transported the mud washed into it and, acting on the third fundamental principle, "deposition," deposited its load when it reached quiet water.

Erosion, transportation and deposition are three fundamental geologic processes which we can see at work all about us. If with these processes in mind we look through the eyes of a billion years, the "everlasting hills" become only the uneroded remnants of hills once larger and different in shape. The pleasant valleys we love to look upon were once smaller and of different form.

Erosion and transportation are bit by bit continuously carving the face of the earth into new forms. Those who see and understand take delight not only in rebuilding in imagination the forms that have been worn away but also in picturing in the mind's eye those forms that natural processes will develop in the future.

The Discoveries of a Scotch Farmer

. . . In view of the strong hold that tradition has on our thoughts, even today, it is not strange that the simple processes of erosion, transportation and deposition, so clearly observable in the Wisconsin millpond, were not understood even by the most advanced scientific men much over a hundred years ago [*Ed. note: late 18th Century*].

It was reserved for a Scotch farmer, a retired physician named Hutton, to see them in their true nature and in all their vast significance.

We can picture him in his strolls along the sandy beaches of his seacoast farm. At his right was the water with its ceaselessly active waves, at his left were cliffs of sandstone and limestone in alternating beds. On a quiet day the waves contented themselves with making beautiful ripple marks on the sandy beach. On rough days they beat wildly at the cliffs and tore them into fragments, which were worn into pebbles and sand grains and added to the beach.

In imagination we can walk along with him and admire the sculpture of the ripple marks just below the water's edge. When we come to a fresh slab of sandstone, beaten from the cliff by a recent storm, and find that it shows the same beautifully carved ripple marks which we see in the loose sand of the beach, we can take with him the first simple step toward a great discovery. We can conclude (as he did) that the ripple marks on the sandstone block must have been made by the waves on a beach of some long gone age. We can clamber over the cliffs and find all through the sandstone other ripple-marked beds that had been buried by the sand of succeeding beds and thus preserved for us to see. Next we can conclude that the shore on which this sandstone was being deposited must have been sinking land and that each rippled beach was covered by the later ones deposited over it. It then becomes obvious that later on these old beach sands must have been raised above the sea and hardened into sandstone, only to be attacked by the waves of the present day and partly worn away, the remainder being left as the present cliffs.

Finally, we can go over in our minds the full cycle of events: (1) fresh beach sands being deposited on a sinking shore; (2) this sand deposit being raised above the sea and cemented into sandstone; and (3) the sandstone then being attacked by the waves and worn down into sand to build a new beach. These are the familiar principles seen in the Wisconsin millpond: (1) *deposition* and raising and hardening; (2) *erosion* by the waves; and (3) *transportation* along the beach.

As our Scotch farmer gradually reached the fullness of these conclusions—and such conclusions do not come so quickly as they are pictured above, but only by slow, logical analysis and anxious, careful thought—he could look back into the past and imagine a numberless succession of such cycles of erosion, transportation and deposition. He could picture the cliffs on innumerable successions of beaches in bygone ages being worn down, transported by the waves, deposited on the beach and raised up above the sea, only to repeat the cycle. He could turn to the future and see the present rippled beach sands under his feet raised above the sea hardened into rock and again eroded into cliffs in endless successions of this cycle. Small wonder then that he wrote, "I see no vestige of a beginning, no prospect of an end." There must have come to him at that time the vision of the vast sweep of the ages which go to make up the story of the billion years of the earth's history. His simple but epoch-making discoveries started geological science on the way to reading that history in the rocks.

The great discoveries of science, once made, appear so simple that they are almost disappointing. A Franklin flies a kite and finds that lightning is the same as electricity. A Faraday, moving a boy's toy magnet, finds that an electric current is produced in a nearby wire, and his simple discovery becomes the foundation of our whole electrical industry. When he was rather scornfully asked by a legislator as to the usefulness of his discovery (which was at once recognized as a great scientific principle) Faraday testily replied, "Perhaps you can tax it someday." And the legislators have.

Our Scotch farmer, Hutton, probably would not have dared even to suggest that the consequences of his discoveries would ever be of material use to mankind; much less would he have had the temerity to suggest that they might someday be taxable. But out of them grew the long continued series of geological observations that have helped us find and use the tremendous wealth of mineral resources which make living conditions in our generation so different from those of a hundred years ago.

Hutton studied the cliffs and noted the succession of beds of different kinds of sandstone and limestone lying one upon another. He crossed a small stream and found that the cliffs on the other side showed the same layers in the same order, and he then concluded that these beds of rock must once have been continuous between the cliffs, for the old beach and sea-bottom deposits could not have been built up in separate hills as they now appeared but must have been continuous like the present beach. He watched the stream in the valley between the cliffs and noted that it was slowly but unceasingly carrying its load of sand and mud from the valley sides into the sea. He studied the little branch valleys and depressions and found that, even though no water was then flowing in some of them, each one carried unmistakable evidence that a rivulet flowed in rainy weather—a rivulet that did its allotted share of work each season in carrying material from along its course into the main stream. So it gradually became certain, as his studies continued, that the whole valley had been carved by the processes of erosion and transportation which he could see in slow but unremitting operation all about him.

The difficult thing to picture was the vast extent of time required to remove the enormous amount of material which once had been where the valley now lay. The change observable in a man's whole lifetime was exceedingly small compared to the total change that Hutton could see must have taken place. And yet here were the processes slowly at work, and here was the result. There was no escaping the conclusion that the processes *must have worked long enough to produce the result*. Truly, in the millions of years that go to make the billion and more of the story the rocks tell us, there must have been ample time for many cycles of this kind. There must have been time for many valleys to have been carved in uplifted sea deposits—time for many long, slow, alternate uplifts and depressions of the places where most of us live, so that under our feet and in the hills about us are the records of periods of alternate sea and land, of deposition and erosion, many times repeated.

Second-Rate Planet

By Carey Croneis and William Krumbein

Among the nine planets that speed endlessly around the sun is this terrestrial sphere. It is neither the largest nor the most massive, and astronomers are apt to remind us not only that it is a second-rate planet but that our sun itself is only a third-rater among the other stars. But because the earth is our abode, to us it is of supreme importance.

One of the first things we learn about the earth is that it is round. Some of us may even remember that a simple proof is that large objects gradually disappear below the horizon as one moves away from them. This is at best only a qualitative argument, but there are several precise proofs. As an example of the scientists' method of attacking such problems, let us follow through the steps involved in determining both the shape and size of the earth.

A little study of a circle will show that the property of circularity involves certain relations between the length of

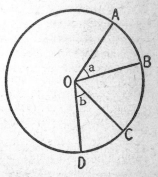

Angle *a* is the same as angle *b*, provided arc *AB* = arc *CD*

an arc of the circle and the angle made by the radii limiting this arc. Note in the accompanying figure that the radii *OA* and *OB* establish the arc *AB*. This arc is so related to the angle *a* that if we choose another arc equal in length to *AB*, such as *CD*, then the angle *b* must be of the same size as angle *a*. In the same manner, an arc twice the length of *AB* will be subtended by an angle twice the size of *a*. We may now argue that if every section through the earth is a circle, then equal distances on its circumference will be subtended by equal angles made by the radii from the center of the earth to the ends of the arcs. In order to measure these internal angles, we must make use of astronomy. Let us, therefore, imagine two observatories about twenty-one hundred miles apart along a north-south line. In each observatory we shall suspend a plumb line,

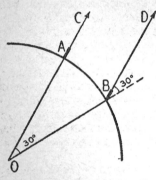

which is nothing more than a string with a weight on the end. This line will point to the center of the earth if the earth is round. Now at the first observatory a telescope is pointed at a star directly overhead. At the same instant, the telescope in the second observatory is pointed at the same star; but because the second observatory is some twenty-one hundred miles from the first, the star obviously will no longer be directly overhead. Thus there will be an

Two observatories 2,100 miles apart simultaneously observe the same star

angle between the plumb line and the direction of the telescope. This angle is measured, and it is found to be about 30°. We now make a diagram like the adjacent one. At *A* is the first observatory, with the plumb line and the telescope pointed directly overhead at the star (which is too distant to be included in the same diagram). At *B* is the second observatory, with its telescope also pointed at the same star, but with an angle between the telescope and the plumb line. Note, however, that the two telescopes themselves are parallel, because the distance to the star is so great that the rays of light reaching the earth from it are practically parallel at any point on the earth.

Remembering that the angle between the telescope and

the plumb line of the second observatory is 30°, we next project the plumb lines into the interior of the earth, where they meet. The angle made by their junction is also 30°, because the lines *AC* and *BD* are parallel, and the line *OB* cutting these parallel lines makes an equal angle with each. Thus, it follows that an angle of 30° at the earth's center subtends a distance of about twenty-one hundred miles along the surface. If we next divide through by thirty, we see that an angle of 1° must subtend a distance of some seventy miles.

Should the same experiment be repeated elsewhere on the earth, and the net result prove to be the same, then we might safely conclude that the earth is spherical. Such measurements have actually been made at many places over the surface of the earth, and everywhere the general relations hold, so that there is no doubt that the earth is spherical. Precisely speaking, of course, the earth is a spheroid, and flattened slightly at the poles. This flattening is so slight that between the polar and equatorial diameters there is a difference of only twenty-seven miles, which is less than one-half of 1 per cent. It is, in fact, so insignificant that it amounts to only about a half inch on a ten-foot globe, and consequently is not shown even on the largest of such representations of the earth.

We have by these experiments found not only that the earth is spherical but also that every degree of the interior angle subtends about seventy miles on the surface. Since there are 360° in a complete circle, we need only multiply our seventy miles by 360 to obtain the *circumference,* or distance around the earth. When this is done, the result is approximately twenty-five thousand miles. Once we have the value of the earth's circumference, we can easily find its *diameter,* or the distance through the earth. We simply divide the circumference by 3.1416 (the value of the old familiar *pi* of school days) and the answer is about eight thousand miles, which is the approximate diameter of the earth.

As long as we are on the subject of measurements, let us pursue it a bit further. If we know the diameter of the earth, we can find its *volume,* because the volume of any ball is 3.1416/6 times the diameter cubed. If we put in our known values, we find that the volume of the earth is nearly two hundred and sixty billion cubic miles. Similarly, since the surface of a sphere is equal to *pi* times the diameter squared, we may compute the *surface area* of the earth. Such a computation shows us that there are about one hundred and ninety-seven million square miles on its broad surface. But large as this area may seem, it is only about one twelve-thousandth the area of the sun's great surface. In other words, the earth's surface area is as much smaller than the sun's as tiny Switzerland is smaller than the earth's entire extent of land and sea.

Another important item concerns the *mean density* of the earth, or its mass per unit volume. To find this, it is necessary first to determine the mass of the entire earth and then to divide this by its volume. The mass of the earth can be determined by several methods, but perhaps the simplest is that known as the *Cavendish experiment*. By this procedure the attraction of two large lead balls for two small silver balls is measured, and then compared to the attraction between the earth and one of the smaller balls. From the exceedingly delicate measurements made in this experiment it is found that the mass of the earth is 6×10^{21} tons, which is the number six followed by twenty-one ciphers. To obtain the mean density of the earth, then, we divide the mass by its volume; whereupon the density is found to be approximately 5.5. In other words, a cubic foot of average earth-substance weighs about 5.5 times as much as a cubic foot of water. But right here we stumble onto an interesting thing. The average density of the familiar rocks of the earth's surface is only about 2.7. Thus the density of the earth's interior must be greater than 5.5, in order to counterbalance the lightness of the surface materials. . . .

For the purposes of later discussions we also ought to have before us a fairly complete picture of the earth's motions in space.

Most proofs of the *earth's rotation* are difficult to grasp without some knowledge of physics. The one usually cited depends on the fact that a heavy pendulum tends to swing in a fixed direction in space as long as no outside forces disturb it. Evidently, then, if such a pendulum is set into motion on a rotating earth, the earth should rotate beneath the pendulum without affecting the direction of swing of the pendulum. Such, in fact, is the result of the pendulum experiment. When first set into motion, it is directed so that the bob swings in a north-south plane. As time goes on, it is found that the pendulum continually departs from this direction, and that in the Northern Hemisphere the plane of swing tends to rotate in a northeast-southwest direction.* It must be borne in mind, however, that an observer on the earth has the same motion as the earth, and therefore he will feel himself at rest and will notice that the direction of swing of the pendulum appears to change. This departure would increase indefinitely were it not for friction stopping the swing of the pendulum. This experiment was first performed by Foucault in Paris, in 1851, and in his honor the device is called the Foucault pendulum. . . . It is interesting to note that observation and theory agree so well that there is no doubt of the actual rotation of the earth upon its axis.

The motion of the earth about the sun, or the *revolution* of the earth, also can be demonstrated in several ways. One of the simplest is by the periodic shift in the position

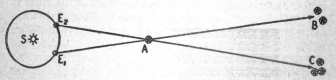

The apparent shift of the nearby star proves the earth's revolution. The sizes and distances are obviously not true to scale

of the nearby stars with respect to the more remote stars. In the adjoining figure the earth's orbit around the sun, *S,* is shown diagrammatically. The earth itself appears in two successive positions, E_1 and E_2, several months apart in its journey around the sun. Star *A* is one of the nearer stars; and in the distance are two groups of stars, *B* and *C,* representing more remote constellations. Notice that when the earth is at E_1, the star *A,* as viewed from the earth, appears to be in group *B,* but that later, when the earth is at E_2, star *A* appears to have moved to a position

* The direction of change depends on whether the observer is north or south of the equator, and the rate of change depends on his latitude. In the latitude of Chicago the plane of swing changes about 10° an hour. At the equator itself there is no change.

among group *C*. Thus star *A* periodically appears to shift back and forth between groups *B* and *C*. Such shifts actually are noted among the nearer stars, and the phenomenon is cited as the *parallax proof* of the earth's revolution.

The *inclination of the earth's axis* to the plane of its orbit is another feature of this second-rate planet into which we should briefly inquire. This inclination is demonstrated by the fact that at any point on the earth's surface the altitude of the sun above the horizon at noon on June 21st and December 21st differs by 47°. This apparent change in the altitude of the sun measures twice the angle of inclination of the earth's axis, which thus turns out to be 23½°. In the adjacent figure the line *OS*, from the center of the earth to the center of the sun, lies in the plane of the orbit. Now at *O* let us erect a perpendicular *OA*, and then draw the earth's axis, *OP*, at an angle of 23½° to *OA*. This angle, *POA*, measures the inclination of the earth's axis.

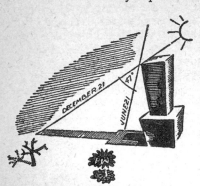

The angle of the sun's rays differs by 47° in June and December; a proof of the inclination of the earth's axis

Inasmuch as the equator of the earth is at right angles to its axis, it follows that the equator is inclined 23½° to the plane of the earth's orbit. This is line *EOE'*. It is the inclination of the earth's axis that causes the seasonal changes on the earth, as the figure below shows. The earth, like any rotating body, tends to keep its axis always oriented in the same

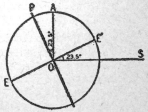

Diagram of the inclination of the earth's axis

direction in space, regardless of the earth's positions in its orbit. Notice, then, that when the earth is at the right in the diagram, the region receiving perpendicular rays from the sun lies 23½° *north* of the equator; whereas when the earth is at the left, the perpendicular rays strike the surface 23½° *south* of the equator. In the course of a year, then, the sun seems to swing through an angle of twice 23½°, or 47°, in its apparent motion above and below the equator. When the earth is at the right, it is summer in the Northern Hemisphere, because at that time the northern half of the earth is receiving the more nearly perpendicular rays from the sun. In like manner, summer in the Southern Hemisphere and winter north of the equator occur when the earth is on the left. . . .

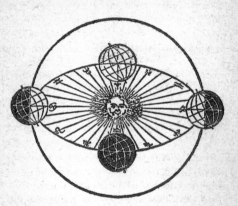

The earth in its journey around the sun. Old engraving from Blaev's *Institution Astronomique* (Amsterdam, 1669)

By this time the reader should have in his mind's eye a fairly clear picture of the earth as a sphere rotating daily on its axis, like a fowl on a spit, as it annually revolves about the warming fire of that unfailing solar hearth, the sun. Second-rate though it may be, this terrestrial sphere of ours has taken part in the stately procession of day and night, summer and winter, since time immemorial; and judging from its astronomical relations, it bids fair to continue into a future immeasurably long.

Interpretations of Nature

By Arthur Holmes

The world we live in presents an endless variety of fascinating problems which excite our wonder and curiosity. The scientific worker, like a detective, attempts to formulate these problems in accurate terms and, so far as is humanly possible, to solve them in the light of all the relevant facts that can be collected by observation and experiment. Such questions as What? How? Where? and When? challenge him to find the clues that may suggest possible replies. Confronted by the many problems presented by, let us say, an active volcano, we may ask: What are the lavas made of? How does the volcano work and how is the heat generated? Where do the lavas and gases come from? When did the volcano first begin to erupt and when is it likely to erupt again?

Here and in all such queries the question What? refers to the stuff things are made of, and an answer can be given in terms of chemical compounds and elements. Not the elements of ancient philosophers, who considered the ultimate ingredients of things to be earth, air, fire and water, but chemical elements such as oxygen, silicon, iron and aluminum.

The question How? refers to processes—the way things are made or happen or change. The ancients regarded natural processes as manifestations of power by capricious and irresponsible gods. . . .

Today we think of natural processes as manifestations of energy acting on or through matter. We no longer blindly accept events as results of the unpredictable whims of mythological beings. Typhoons and hurricanes are no longer interpreted as the destructive breath of a wind god: they arise from the heating of the air over sun-scorched lands. The source of the energy is heat from the sun. Volcanic eruptions and earthquakes no longer reflect the erratic behavior of the gods of the underworld: they arise from the action of the earth's internal heat on and through the surrounding crust. The source of the energy lies in the material of the inner earth. In many directions, of course, and particularly where great catastrophes are concerned, our knowledge is still woefully incomplete. Only the first of the questions we have asked about volcanoes can as yet be satisfactorily answered. The point is not that we now pretend to understand everything—if we did, the task of science would be over—but that we have faith in the orderliness of natural processes. As a result of two or three centuries of scientific investigation we have come to believe that Nature is understandable in the sense that when we ask her questions by way of appropriate observation and experiment, she will answer truly and reward us with discoveries that endure. . . .

The Scope and Subdivisions of Geology

Modern geology has for its aim the deciphering of the whole evolution of the earth and its inhabitants from the time of the earliest records that can be recognized in the rocks right down to the present day. So ambitious a program requires much subdivision of effort, and in practice it is convenient to divide the subject into a number of branches. . . . The key words of the three main branches are the *materials* of the earth's rocky framework (mineralogy and petrology); the geological processes or *machinery* of the earth, by means of which changes of all kinds are brought about (physical geology); and finally the succession of these changes, or the *history* of the earth (historical geology).

The earth is made up of a great variety of materials, such as air, water, ice and living organisms, as well as minerals and rocks and the useful deposits of metallic ores and fuels which are associated with them. The relative movements of these materials (wind, rain, rivers, waves, currents and glaciers; the growth and movement of plants and animals; and the movements of hot materials inside the earth, as witnessed by volcanic activity) all bring about changes in the earth's crust and on its surface. The changes involve the development of new rocks from old; new structures in the crust; and new distributions of land and sea, mountains and plain, and even of climate and weather. The scenery of today is only the latest stage of an ever changing kaleidoscopic series of widely varied landscapes—and sea-scapes. *Physical geology* is concerned with all the ter-restrial agents and processes of change and with the effects brought about by them. This branch of geology is by no means restricted to geomorphology, the study of the sur-face relief of the present day, which it shares with physical geography. Its main interest, as we have seen, is in the machinery of the earth, past and present, and in the var-ious by-products, of which the existing surface relief and the rocks now in process of formation are important ex-amples.

In the crust of the earth changes of all kinds have been going on continuously for well over three thousand million years. To a geologist a rock is more than an aggregate of minerals; it is a page of the earth's autobiography with a story to unfold, if only he can read the language in which the record is written. Placed in their proper order from first to last (*stratigraphy*), these pages embody the history of the earth. Moreover, it is familiar knowledge that many beds of rock contain the remains or impressions of shells or bones or leaves. These objects, called fossils, are the relics of animals or plants that inhabited the earth in ancient times. *Paleontology* is the study of the remains of these ancestral forms of life. Thus we see that *historical geology* deals not only with the sequence of events brought about by the operation of the physical processes, but also with the his-tory of the long procession of life through the ages.

Geology is by no means without practical importance in relation to the needs and industries of mankind. Thou-sands of geologists are actively engaged in locating and exploring the mineral resources of the earth. The whole world is being searched for coal and oil and for the ores of the useful metals. Geologists are also directly concerned with the vital subject of water supply. Many engineering projects, such as tunnels, canals, docks and reservoirs, call for geological advice in the selection of sites and materials. In these and many other ways, geology is applied to the service of mankind.

Although geology has its own laboratory methods for

studying minerals, rocks and fossils, it is essentially an open-air science. It attracts its followers to crags and waterfalls, glaciers and volcanoes, beaches and coral reefs, ever farther and farther afield in the search for information about the earth and her often puzzling behavior. Wherever rocks are to be seen in cliffs and quarries, their arrangement and sequence can be observed and their story deciphered. With his hammer and maps the geologist in the field leads a healthy and exhilarating life. His powers of observation become quickened, his love of Nature in all her moods is deepened, and the thrill of discovery is ever at hand.

The Outer Zones of the Earth

As it presents itself to direct experience, the earth can be physically described as a ball of rock (the lithosphere), partly covered by water (the hydrosphere) and wrapped in an envelope of air (the atmosphere). To these three physical zones it is convenient to add a biological zone (the biosphere).

The *atmosphere* is the layer of gases and vapor which envelops the earth. It is essentially a mixture of nitrogen and oxygen with smaller quantities of water vapor, carbon dioxide and inert gases such as argon. Geologically it is important as the medium of climate and weather, of wind, cloud, rain and snow.

The *hydrosphere* includes all the natural waters of the outer earth. Oceans, seas, lakes and rivers cover about three-quarters of the surface. But this is not all. Underground, for hundreds and even thousands of feet in some places, the pore spaces and fissures of the rocks are also filled with water. This ground water, as it is called, is tapped in springs and wells, and is sometimes encountered in disastrous quantities in mines. Thus there is a somewhat irregular but nearly continuous mantle of water around the earth, saturating the rocks, and over the enormous depressions of the ocean floors completely submerging them. If it were uniformly distributed over the earth's surface it would form an ocean about nine thousand feet deep.

The *biosphere,* the sphere of life, is probably a less familiar conception. But think of the great forests and prairies with their countless swarms of animals and insects. Think of the tangles of seaweed, of the widespread banks of mollusks, or reefs of coral and shoals of fishes. Add to these the inconceivable numbers of bacteria and other microscopic plants and animals. Myriads of these minute organisms are present in every cubic inch of air and water and soil. Taken altogether, the diverse forms of life constitute an intricate and ever changing network, clothing the surface with a tapestry that is nearly continuous. Even high snows and desert sands fail to interrupt it completely, and lava fields fresh from the craters of volcanoes are quickly invaded by the pressure of life outside. Such is the sphere of life, and both geologically and geographically it is of no less importance than the physical zones.

The *lithosphere* is the outer solid shell or crust of the earth. It is made of rocks in great variety, and on the lands it is commonly covered by a blanket of soil or other loose deposits, such as desert sands. The depth to which the lithosphere extends downward is a matter of definition: it depends on our conception of the crust and what lies beneath. It is usual to regard the crust as a heterogeneous shell, possibly about twenty to thirty miles thick, in which the rocks at any given level are not everywhere the same. Beneath the crust, in what may be called the *substratum,* or *mantle,* the material at any given level appears to be practically uniform, at least in those physical properties that can be tested.

The dominant rocks occurring in the crust fall into two contrasted groups:

(*a*) Light rocks, including granite and related types, having an average specific gravity or density* of about 2.7. Chemically these rocks are very rich in *si*lica, while *a*lumina is the most abundant of the remaining constituents. Since it is often desirable to refer to them as a whole, such rocks are collectively known by the mnemonic term *sial.*

(*b*) Dark and heavy rocks, including basalt and related types (density about 2.9–3.0) and still heavier rocks (rang-

---

*The *specific gravity* of a substance $= \dfrac{\text{the mass of any volume of the substance}}{\text{the mass of an equal volume of water}}$

The *Density* of a substance is the mass of unit volume of the substance, generally expressed as the mass in grams of one cubic centimeter. Since 1 c.c. of water has a mass of 1 gm., the density of water is 1. In c.g.s. units specific gravity and density are numerically the same.

ing in density up to about 3.4. In these *si*lica (40–50 per cent) is still the leading constituent, though it is much less abundant than in granite (70 per cent). In the heavier rocks of this group *ma*gnesia takes second place, and the whole group is conveniently known as *sima*. When it is necessary to make the distinction, the basaltic rocks are sometimes referred to as *salsima*. The sial is the dominant material of the continental crust down to a depth of several

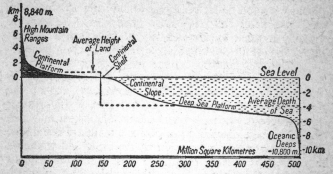

Hypsographic curve, showing the areas of the earth's solid surface between successive levels from the highest mountain peaks to the deepest oceanic deeps

miles, while the sima forms the foundations of the ocean floor and extends beneath the continents. Products of the sima group, represented by basaltic lavas, are brought to the surface by many continental and oceanic volcanoes.

Continents and Ocean Floors

The surface of the crust reaches very different levels in different places. The areas of land and sea floor between successive levels have been estimated, and the results can be graphically represented as shown in the figure. From this diagram it is clear that there are two dominant levels: the continental platform and the oceanic or deep-sea platform. The slope connecting them, which is actually quite gentle, is called the continental slope.

The continental platform includes a submerged outer border, known as the *continental shelf*, which extends beyond the shore zone to an average depth of about one hundred fathoms or two hundred meters. Structurally, the real ocean basins must be regarded as commencing, not at the visible shoreline, but at the edge of the shelf. The basins, however, are more than full, and the overflow of sea water inundates about eleven million square miles of the continental platform. The North Sea, the Baltic and

SOME NUMERICAL FACTS ABOUT THE EARTH

Size

	Km.	Miles
Equatorial diameter of the earth	12,757	7,926.7
Polar diameter of the earth	12,714	7,900.0
Equatorial circumference	40,077	24,902
Polar circumference	40,000	24,860

Area

	Millions of	
	Sq. km.	Sq. miles
Area of the sea floor (70.78 per cent)	361	139.4
Area of the land (29.22 per cent)	149	57.5
Total area of the earth	510	196.9

Volume, Density and Mass

		Millions of	
		Cu. km.	Cu. miles
Volume of earth		1,082,000	259,000
Density of the earth	5.517		
Mass of the earth	5,876 million million million tons		

Relief

	Meters	Feet
Greatest known height: Mount Everest	8,840	29,141 above sea level
Average height of the land	825	2,707 above sea level
Mean level of the surface (land and sea)	250	820 above sea level
Mean level of the lithosphere	2,450	7,040 below sea level
Average depth of the sea	3,800	12,460 below sea level
Greatest known depth: Challenger Deep	10,950	35,600 below sea level

Hudson Bay are examples of shallow seas (epicontinental or shelf seas) which lie on the continental shelf. It is of interest to notice that during the Ice Age, when enormous quantities of water were abstracted from the oceans to form the great ice sheets that then lay over Europe and North

America, much of the continental shelf must have been land. Conversely, if the ice now covering Antarctica and Greenland were to melt away, the sea level would rise and the continents would be still further submerged.

The continents themselves have a varied relief of plains, plateaus and mountain ranges, the last rising to a maximum height of twenty-nine thousand one hundred and forty-one feet (Mount Everest). The ocean floors, except locally, are less vigorously diversified than the continents, but islands, sea mounts, submarine ridges and plateaus rise from their normally monotonous surfaces, and basins and deeps sink to more than average depths. The deepest sounding so far made is thirty-five thousand six hundred feet (Challenger Deep, off the Philippines). The diagram might suggest that the greatest deeps are farthest away from the lands, but such is not the case. The deeps lie close in to the continental edge, and along the Asiatic side of the Pacific they are particularly strongly developed.

From the figures given above it is clear that the total vertical range of the surface of the lithosphere is just over twelve miles. To grasp the true relation between the surface relief and the earth itself draw a circle with a radius of two inches. A moderately thin pencil line has a thickness of about 1/100 inch. If two inches represents four thousand miles, then the thickness of the outline of the circle represents twenty miles. On this scale the relief is all contained well within the thickness of a pencil line.

Nevertheless, the relief is very great by human standards, and the question arises how it is that there are such differences of level. The earth might very well have been a smooth globe with a uniform oceanic cover. Just how it comes about that continental land areas exist at all is still an unsolved problem. But there is no mystery in the fact that the continents stand up like platforms above the ocean floor. Like ships riding light, the continents protrude just because their rocks (sial) are light compared with the heavier rocks (sima) that underlie the ocean floor. In the same way, mountain ranges stand high above the continental platforms because the sialic rocks beneath them go down to correspondingly greater depths. High mountains have deep "roots" (*see* Figure, P. 37). To understand how these curious facts came to be ascertained, it is convenient to begin by considering the effects of gravitation and rotation on the shape of the earth.

The Shape of the Earth

The first voyage around the world, begun at Seville by Magellan in 1519 and completed at Seville by del Cano in 1522, established beyond dispute that the earth is a globe. Today, aviators could fly around the earth in any direction in a few days. But long ago the nearly spherical form of the earth had been inferred from a variety of observations, *e.g.*, the circular boundary of the earth's shadow on the moon during an eclipse, and the circularity of the horizon, wherever observed, combined with the fact that its distance* increases with the altitude of the observer.

The reason for the spherical shape of the earth became clear when Newton discovered the law of gravitation. All the particles of the earth are pulled toward the center of gravity and the spherical shape is the natural response to the maximum possible concentration. Even if a body the size of the earth were stronger than steel, it could not maintain a shape such as, let us say, that of a cube. The pressure exerted by the weight of the edges and corners would squeeze out material in depth. Equilibrium would be reached only when the faces had bulged out, and the edges and corners had sunk in, until every part of the surface was equidistant from the center.

The earth is not exactly spherical, however. Again it was Newton who first showed that, because of the earth's daily rotation, its matter is affected not only by inward gravitation, but also by an outward centrifugal force, which reaches its maximum at the equator. He deduced that there should be an equatorial bulge, where the apparent value of gravity was reduced, and a complementary polar flattening, where the centrifugal force becomes vanishingly small. If this were so, the length of a degree of latitude across the equator would be shorter than in the far north. Expeditions were despatched to Peru in 1735 and to Lapland in 1736

---

* The distance of the horizon in miles is given very closely by the simple expression $\sqrt{3h/2}$, where h is the altitude of the eye in feet. From an airplane at the height of twenty thousand feet, for example, the aviator can see places 174 miles away.

to test this idea, and Newton's deduction was confirmed. If the surface of the earth were everywhere at sea level its shape would closely approximate to that of an ellipsoid of rotation (or spheroid) with a polar diameter of 7,900 miles nearly twenty-seven miles shorter than the equatorial diameter.

How is it, then, that the earth is not exactly a spheroid? The reason is that the crustal rocks are not everywhere of the same density. Since the equatorial bulge is a consequence of the relatively low value of gravity around the equatorial zone, it follows that there should be bulges in other places where gravity is relatively low; that is to say, wherever the outer part of the crust is composed of light sialic rocks. Such places are the continents. On the other hand, wherever the outer part of the crust is composed of heavy rocks (sima) the surface should be correspondingly depressed. Such regions are the ocean basins.

The earth is in gravitational equilibrium. If there were no rotation and no lateral differences in the density of the rocks, the earth would be a sphere. As a result of rotation it becomes a spheroid. As a further result of density differences in the crustal rocks, continents, mountain ranges and oceanic basins occur as irregularities superimposed upon the surface of the spheroid.

Isostasy

For the ideal condition of gravitational equilibrium that controls the heights of continents and ocean floors, in accordance with the densities of their underlying rocks, the term *isostasy* (Greek *isostasios,* "in equipoise") was proposed by Dutton, an American geologist, in 1889. The idea may be grasped by thinking of a series of wooden blocks of different heights floating in water. The blocks emerge by amounts which are proportional to their respective heights; they are said to be in a state of hydrostatic balance. Isostasy is the corresponding state of balance existing between extensive blocks of the earth's crust, which in consequence rise to different levels and appear at the surface as mountain ranges, widespread plateaus or plains. The idea implies that there is a certain minimum level below the surface, where the pressure due to the weight of the material in each unit column of the crust is everywhere the same. This isopiestic (uniform pressure) level may be regarded as the base of the crust or lithosphere. The earth's major relief is said to be *compensated* by the differences of

Wooden blocks of different heights floating in water (shown in front as a section through the tank), to illustrate the conception of isostatic balance between adjacent columns of the earth's crust

density within the crust, and the level where the compensation is complete, *i.e.*, the isopiestic level, is often referred to as the *level of compensation*. Naturally, individual peaks and valleys are not separately balanced in this way; the minor relief features of the surface are easily maintained by the strength of the crustal rocks. . . . Perfect isostasy is rarely attained, though there is generally a remarkably close approach.

If a mountain range were simply a protuberance of rock resting on the continental platform and wholly supported by the strength of the foundation, then a plumb line—such as is used for leveling surveying instruments—would be deflected from the true vertical by an amount proportional to the gravitational attraction of the mass of the mountain range. The first hint that mountains are not merely masses stuck on the crust was provided by the Peru expedition of 1735. Bouguer found that the deflection of the plumb line by the Andes was surprisingly small, and he expressed his suspicion that the gravitational attraction of the Andes "is much smaller than that to be expected from the mass represented by these mountains." Similar discrepancies were met with during the survey of the Indian lowlands south of the Himalayan Mountains. The attraction of the enormous mass of the Himalayas was estimated to be suf-

ficient to deflect the plumb line by at least 15″ of arc, but
the real deflection found by Everest was only 5″ of arc.
Even more remarkable was the observation that along the
south coast of the Bay of Biscay the plumb line is actually
deflected toward the Bay instead of toward the Pyrenees.

Only one physical explanation of these discrepancies is
available. There must be a deficiency of mass in the crustal
columns underlying the visible mountain ranges, *i.e.*, the
density of the rocks must be relatively low down to considerable depths. The possible density distributions are,

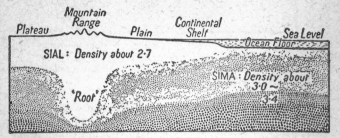

Diagrammatic section through the earth's crust to illustrate the
relationship between surface features and the probable distribution
of sial and sima in depth. Based on gravity determinations and exploration of the crustal layers by earthquake waves

of course, infinite. Fortunately, we know something of
the rocks within the crust and can say what the probable
densities are. Moreover, earthquake waves can be used to
explore the depths, and evidence from this source indicates
that mountain ranges have sialic roots going down to
depths of forty kilometers or more; that under plains near
sea level the thickness of the sial is only ten or twelve kilometers; and that beneath the ocean floor the sial is either
absent or quite thin. The figure illustrates an approximation to the structure of the crust in relation to the surface
relief.

The Distribution of Land and Sea

Certain peculiarities in the distribution of land and sea
have aroused discussion ever since the main features of
the earth's surface were discovered.

1. The marked concentration of land in the Northern Hemisphere and of water in the Southern, combined with the reversal of this contrast in the polar regions.

2. The occurrence of 81 per cent of all the land in the "Land Hemisphere," which has its pole in Brittany and includes North America, Europe, Asia and Africa and more than half of South America; and the predominance of water in the corresponding "Water Hemisphere," which has its pole near New Zealand. The following figures bring out these differences:

	Percentage of land
"Land Hemisphere"	49
Northern Hemisphere	39
Whole earth	29
Southern Hemisphere	19
"Water Hemisphere"	9

3. The southerly extension of the three continental blocks of South America, Africa and Australia.

4. The antipodal relation between land and sea. About forty-four per cent of the surface has sea opposite sea, but little more than one per cent has land opposite land. Ninety-five per cent of the land is antipodal to sea. . . .

Now we have already seen that the continents are essentially rafts of light sial, surrounded by ocean floors of heavy sima. It is for this reason that the continents stand high above the ocean floors. . . .

The material of the sial may be regarded as a kind of light slag which accumulated at the surface during the earth's consolidation from a molten state. We should expect it to have accumulated uniformly, so that it would everywhere form the upper layer of the crust. Where, then, is the sialic material that is missing from the ocean floors? Obviously, it must be either in the earth or outside the earth, and speculative answers have been based on each of these alternatives.

If part of the sial was removed from the earth, the moon is the most probable place to look for it. The moon may have separated from the earth at a very early stage in the history of our planet. If a sial shell had already formed before the moon was born, much of it must have been carried away when the great rupture occurred. Long ago it was suggested that the vast Pacific basin might be a relic of the scar that was left behind, and it has since been discovered that this is by far the greatest of the regions from which a cover of sial is lacking. This hypothesis is an attractive one, but unfortunately it has to meet the great difficulty that the moon could only have separated while the parent planet was still in a molten state, *i.e.*, before there could have been a sial shell. By the time the sial had formed the interior would almost certainly have become too stiff for separation of the moon to be mechanically possible.

If the missing sial is still in the crust, it must be con-

Convection currents in a layer of liquid uniformly heated from below

centrated in the continental rafts. A clue as to how such a concentration might be brought about is provided by observing the behavior of the light scum on the surface of jam which is gently boiling. The heat from below keeps the jam slowly circulating. A hot current ascends near the middle, and, turning along at the surface, it sweeps the scum to the edges, where the current descends. The scum is too light to be carried down, and so it accumulates until it is skimmed off. When the earth was molten it would cool by means of similar circulations. Convection currents would rise in certain places, spread out horizontally, and then turn down again. There are reasons for suspecting that a subcrustal circulation may still be going on within the earth, though now at an excessively slow rate. However, when the circulation was vigorous, the horizontal currents spreading out from each ascending current may have swept certain regions clear of sial. These would become ocean basins. Where the horizontal currents of one convecting system met those of a neighboring system they would be obliged to turn down, and the light sial would thus become concentrated in the regions overlying the descending currents. These regions would become continents. The "convection current" hypothesis is plausible, but as yet it is no more than an intelligent guess. The origin of the continents remains an unsolved geological problem.

Geological Processes

. . . The leading geological processes . . . fall into two contrasted groups. The first group—denudation and deposition—includes the processes which act on the crust or at or very near its surface, as a result of the movements and chemical activities of air, water, ice and living organisms. Such processes are essentially of external origin. The second group—earth movements, igneous activity and metamorphism—includes the processes which act within or through the crust, as a result of the physical and chemical activities of the materials of the substratum (or mantle) and of gases and magmas formed in the crust or passing through it. Such processes are essentially of internal origin.

Both groups of processes operate under the control of gravitation (including attractions due to the sun and moon), co-operating with the earth's bodily movements—rotation about its axis and revolution around the sun. But if these were all, the earth's surface would soon reach a state of approximate equilibrium from which no further changes of geological significance could develop. Each

CLASSIFICATION OF GEOLOGICAL PROCESSES

I. Processes of External Origin

1. *Denudation* (Weathering, erosion and transport)
    Sculpturing of the land surface and removal of the products of rock decay mechanically and in solution

2. *Deposition*
    (*a*) of the debris transported mechanically
        (*e.g.*, sand and mud)
    (*b*) of the materials transported in solution:
        (i) by evaporation and chemical precipitation
            (*e.g.*, rock salt)
        (ii) by the intervention of living organisms
            (*e.g.*, coral limestone)
    (*c*) of organic matter, largely the remains of vegetation
        (*e.g.*, peat)

II. Processes of Internal Origin

1. *Earth Movements* (including earthquakes)
   Uplift and depression of land areas and sea floors; and mountain building by lateral compression (folding and overthrusting) of rocks
2. *Igneous Activity*
   The intrusion of magmas and the extrusion of lavas and other
   volcanic products
3. *Metamorphism*
   The transformation of pre-existing rocks into new types by
   the action of heat, pressure, stress and chemically active
   migrating fluids.

group of processes, to be kept going, requires some
additional source of energy. The processes of external
origin are specifically maintained by the radiation of heat
from the sun. Those of internal origin are similarly maintained by the liberation of heat from the stores of energy
locked within the earth.

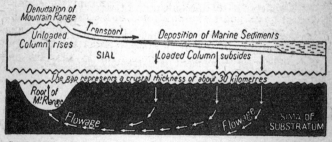

Section illustrating isostatic readjustment in response to denudation
and deposition

Throughout the ages the face of the earth has been
changing its expression. At times its features have been
flat and monotonous. At others—as today—they have
been bold and vigorous. But in the long struggle for
supremacy between the sun-born forces of land destruction and the earth-born forces of land renewal, neither has
permanently gained the mastery.

Isostasy and Geological Processes

It will now be realized that geological processes bring
about changes that must inevitably upset the ideal state

of isostatic balance which gravitation tends to establish. When a mountain range is carved into peaks and valleys and gradually worn down by the agents of denudation, the load on the underlying column of the crust is reduced by the weight of the rock waste that has been carried away. At the same time a neighboring column, underlying a region of delta and sea floor where the rock waste is being deposited, receives a corresponding increase of load. Unless a complementary transfer of material occurs in depth, the two columns cannot remain in isostatic equilibrium. At the base of the crust the pressure exerted by the loaded column is increased, while that exerted by the unloaded column is decreased. In response to this pressure difference in the substratum a slow flowage of material is set up, as illustrated in the figure on P. 41. The loaded column sinks and the unloaded one rises. This process, whereby isostasy is restored, is called *isostatic readjustment*.

The upper part of the substratum consists of hot rock material which probably differs from the crystalline rocks seen at the surface by being much richer in gases. Acting like molecular ball bearings, the gases facilitate flowage, but nevertheless the movement is extremely sluggish. Moreover, in some regions it appears that the substratum material is not altogether devoid of strength. It then behaves as a plastic substance (with a little strength) rather than as a viscous substance (with no strength). In this case no flowage is possible until the departure from isostasy is sufficient to set up a pressure difference that can overcome the strength. The region concerned will therefore remain slightly out of isostatic balance. In practice, perfect isostasy is rarely attained, though there is generally a remarkably close approach.

It may happen that certain geological processes disturb the pre-existing isostatic balance much more rapidly than it can be restored by deep-seated flowage in the substratum. For example, when the thick European and North American ice-sheets began to melt away toward the end of the Ice Age, about twenty-five thousand years ago, these regions were quickly relieved of an immense load of ice. The resulting uplifts which then began are still actively in progress. Far above the shores of Finland and Scandinavia there are raised beaches which show that a maximum uplift of nearly nine hundred feet has already occurred, and every twenty-eight years another foot is added to the total all around the northern end of the Gulf of Bothnia. The region is still out of isostatic balance, and it can be estimated that it has still to rise another seven hundred feet or so before equilibrium can be reached.

A common misunderstanding about isostasy is that it is responsible for earth movements of all kinds. It must, therefore, be clearly realized that isostasy is only a state of balance; it is not a force or a geological agent. It is the disturbance of isostasy by denudation and deposition, earth movements and igneous activity, that brings into play the gravitational forces that restore isostasy. The restoration involves vertical movements of the crust which are additional to the earth movements brought about by the independent activities of the earth's interior.

——

PART TWO

Changes Over the Earth's Surface

THE ESSENCE of this section is contained in the single word "change." It is summed up briefly in the poetic words of one of the greatest of American geologists, G. K. Gilbert:

"Nature is full of change. The bud we saw yesterday is a flower today; the leaf that was broad and green in summer, in autumn is shriveled and brown; the bush we knew in childhood is now a broad, spreading tree. Such changes are easily seen, because they fall within the span of a man's life, and so the principle of perpetual progress in the organic world is familiar to all. Progress in the inorganic world is so slow that it is less easily seen, and there is a widespread impression that the hills are everlasting and unchanging. This impression is false. Not only hills, but mountains, plains and valleys are perpetually acted on by heat and cold, sunshine and rain, wind and stream, and are gradually changed. Not only do they now undergo change, but by such agents it will eventually be transformed into a feature of different type. Thus every element of the landscape has an origin and a history."

In the air above the earth, as on the earth, change is the keynote, as George T. Renner, Professor of Geography at Teachers College, Columbia University, shows clearly in "The Atmospheric Pattern." He describes the three atmospheric shells—the troposphere, the stratosphere, and finally the ionosphere. He considers their composition, their movements, their effects on the earth's surface. He tells how records of barometric pressure are kept at stations in different parts of the world in order to interpret this aerial topography. Finally he analyzes the world wind system and shows why it is so strongly affected by the varying output of the sun's radiant energy, and how it affects the weather everywhere. The facts in his article are the fundamentals on which the science of meteorology, the study of weather, is based.

In the first section of this book Professor Holmes presented a brief classification of geologic processes. First of these processes is that of denudation, of weathering, erosion and transport. In "Crumbling Rocks" Raymond Janssen, head of the Geology Department at Marshall College, Iowa, elaborates this process of sculpturing of the land surface, and again emphasizes the effect of change on the earth's face. In the following articles, details of the process are discussed by a geologist, a steamboat pilot, an oceanographer and an artist.

The geologist Herdman Cleland, formerly Professor of Geology at Williams College, describes the "Erosion Cycle" of streams as they develop from youth through maturity to old age, flowing first through V-shaped valleys, then gradually carving the landscape into rounded valley basins, until in old age the valleys become plains through which streams meander in snakelike pattern.

It is these meanders which Mark Twain, the Mississippi River pilot, describes so graphically in an extract from *Life on the Mississippi*. Again and again, the great river has undercut its banks, deflected the current and shortened its length; and has changed, not only the river course, but also the lives of the people on it.

While streams and rivers are changing the earth's face in an extraordinary way, glaciers in more widely scattered regions are likewise changing its physiognomy. Richard Flint, Professor of Geology at Yale University, specialist in glacial geology, describes these great ice masses that blanket six million square miles of the earth's surface. His conclusions are the result of field expeditions to glacial regions. He uses the methods developed by physicists to sound glacier depths and to trace the rate of glacial flow. Repeatedly throughout this book we shall see that the tools developed in one field are applied in new and wholly unexpected ways to other fields, so that the boundaries between physics and geology or between geology and chemistry no longer exist. The essential unity of science becomes increasingly apparent.

Just as Richard Flint explores glaciers by modern geophysical methods, oceanographers apply similar methods to

"The Study of the Sea." In the next selection Claude E. ZoBell, Assistant Director of the Scripps Institute of Oceanography in La Jolla, California, first offers a brief introduction to the sea and its composition, then leads us over the fantastic landscape of the ocean floor. He shows us the great mountains that rise there, the fantastic deeps, and asks questions about their origin which still have no definite answer. In this new and little explored frontier are problems for the oceanographer, the geophysicist and geochemist, the biologist; and even for the meteorologist and the navigator.

We have journeyed down the Mississippi. We have explored glaciers and oceans. Now John VanDyke introduces us to "The Desert." VanDyke, an artist at heart, a keen observer by nature, looks at the desert and reports what he sees in poetic language which nevertheless is scientifically accurate. He tells of the Salton Basin and of the sea which, in ancient times, covered that area. He shows how the delta of the Colorado River gradually built outward until a great bowl, its bottom nearly three hundred feet below sea level, was left. VanDyke's account was written in 1902. Four years later, in 1906, the Colorado again flooded its banks. Once more the overflow filled the bowl with water, and the present Salton Sea was born.

The Atmospheric Pattern

By George T. Renner

To an astronomer on the moon, peering at us through a telescope, many of the earth's surface features would be clearly visible. Indeed, a surprising amount of detail could be seen by his naked eye. One very important set of features would, however, not be visible. This is the pattern of the earth's atmosphere. Certain atmospheric impurities, such as dust and smoke, and large formations of clouds might be observed, but the air itself would be invisible. We ourselves tend to underestimate the atmosphere because it cannot be seen. It is nevertheless a very real part of our natural environment, and its importance has of late been rapidly increasing.

We live on one sphere and inside another; that is, we live on the outside of a solid globe and on the inside of a hollow globe. This outer gaseous sphere is as much a part of our planet as the inner one. Consequently, we live *in* the earth rather than *on* it, a highly significant circumstance.

Composition of the Atmosphere

The atmosphere generally may be thought of as chiefly a mixture of two invisible gases, nitrogen and oxygen, in which the proportion of nitrogen to oxygen is about four to one. The oxygen supports life; the nitrogen seems to serve no direct function except to dilute the oxygen, in much the same way that soda water dilutes the syrup in a carbonated drink.

Other substances are also present in the atmosphere in varying amounts. The analysis of a sample of air would appear about as follows:

Constituent	Per cent
Nitrogen	78.02
Oxygen	20.71
Argon	.80
Water vapor	.41
Carbon dioxide	.03
Rare gases	.02
Dust and plant spores	.01
	100.00

The various substances in the atmosphere do not form a chemical compound as do the hydrogen and oxygen in water. Instead, they form only a mechanical mixture of separate substances. The gases in the air (other than carbon monoxide) do not vary greatly in proportion from time to time nor from one place to another over the earth, but the amounts of such "impurities" as dust, smoke, spores and water vapor do vary considerably. These impurities have an important bearing upon visibility, rainfall, sunshine, diffusion of light, sky colors and other natural phenomena. . . .

Depth of the Atmosphere

The thickness of the atmosphere is not known. Man has flown planes to a height of eight miles or more, and has ascended in balloons to about fourteen miles. Luminous meteors have been observed at heights of two hundred miles, and northern lights at even greater heights. Physicists have calculated that the atmosphere could theoretically be some twenty-one thousand miles deep, since the earth's gravitation could hold gas molecules captive at about that distance. Beyond that range, gases would gradually drift away and be lost. Though there is reason to believe that there are some gas molecules distributed through interplanetary space, we shall probably never know just how deep our atmosphere really is. We have evidence that it extends outward several hundred miles, and it may extend several thousand.

In any event the exact thickness of the whole atmosphere is of no great importance to man. The thickness, composition and behavior of the lower portion of the atmosphere are, however, of very great importance.

Three Atmospheric Shells

The gaseous envelope of the earth is actually composed of three shells, or hollow spheres, one inside the other.

The Troposphere

The innermost shell is known as the troposphere. It is of variable thickness, extending upward about four miles over the poles, seven miles over latitude 40°, and about eleven miles over the equator. Its average thickness is, therefore, seven or eight miles. This lowest layer is marked by winds, storms and turbulent vertical air movements known as convection. Its upper ceiling is a curved surface known as the tropopause, above which convection currents do not ordinarily rise. The temperature at the bottom of the troposphere is highly variable, ranging from nearly 100° below zero Fahrenheit, to about 130° above zero, depending roughly upon the temperature of the surface of the geosphere or hydrosphere which it touches. In general, the temperature of the lower air decreases 1° Fahrenheit for every three hundred feet upward from the earth's surface. This "lapse rate" of temperature decrease continues up to the tropopause.

Most of the atmospheric dust, moisture, bacteria, smoke and carbon dioxide are found in the troposphere. These elements produce an unending variety of atmospheric conditions. Particularly interesting is the always varying display of cloud forms caused by the condensation of water vapor in the air. In general clouds are of four basic types: First, there are the *cumulus* clouds, white puffy forms resembling burst cotton bales, shaped like cauliflowers or inverted anvils, which result most characteristically from condensation of moisture over rising columns of air. Second, there are the dark, low, formless *nimbus* clouds, which usually accompany rain, snow and hailstorms. Third, there are the *stratus* clouds, which are layers of condensed moisture—layers of haze, lifted fog or dense strata of cloud. Fourth, there are the *cirrus* clouds, light, feathery, combed out or stringy cloud forms—often consisting of frost crystals instead of droplets of water. Besides these four basic cloud types, there is an almost limitless number of alto-fracto, and combination or intermediate forms.

Although we do not know the total thickness or volume of the atmosphere, we do know the total amount of it. Its mass is approximately 1/1,200,000 of the mass of the geosphere and hydrosphere combined. Since this mass of air is pulled downward by gravitation, it is compressed progressively toward its lower levels. This means that at sea level there is a large number of air particles in a cubic foot of space, fewer at intermediate levels, and very few indeed near the top of the atmosphere. If it could all be compressed to the same density as that of the air at sea level, it would make a uniform shell of atmosphere only five miles deep. An airplane could then skim along on top of this elevation, but could go no higher because above that level there would be only a vacuum.

The fact that the atmosphere is not compressed to one almost uniform density (as is ocean water) makes it important to know what the atmospheric pressure is at any given time, place and elevation. To enable us to determine this pressure the barometer has been developed. In its simplest form, a barometer is merely a vertical glass vacuum tube sealed at one end and open at the other, with the open end immersed in a pan of some liquid (usually mercury because it is a heavy fluid). The weight of atmosphere resting upon the surface of the liquid in the pan presses downward and pushes some of the liquid up into the vacuum. The liquid inside the tube comes to rest when its total weight equals the total weight of air in a column of equal cross section from the foot of the tube to the top of the atmosphere. Under average conditions, the atmosphere presses downward upon every square inch of surface at sea level with a force of approximately fifteen pounds. Since a column of mercury one square inch in cross section and thirty inches high also weighs fifteen pounds, the two will exactly balance. Average atmospheric pressure at sea level is often stated as "thirty inches of barometric pressure." Ordinary changes in atmospheric pressure at sea level cause the mercury in the barometer to vary between twenty-nine and thirty-one inches. Under extraordinary conditions it may vary a little more in either direction.

If a barometer is carried below sea level, as into Death Valley or the Dead Sea Lowland, or into a deep mine shaft, the mercury will rise above an average of thirty inches. If a barometer is carried upward in a mountain climb, the mercury which read thirty inches at sea level will read only twenty-nine inches at about one thousand feet. At one mile it will have fallen to twenty-five and a half inches. At two miles it will register twenty inches; at three miles, sixteen inches; and so forth. At the top of Mount Everest, the world's highest peak, it will register only nine inches. At the tropopause or top of the troposphere (which averages a little over seven miles) the barometric pressure will be about seven inches. Judging from the pressure exerted by the mass of the atmosphere, we may conclude that half of all the air lies below 3.6 miles, and that three-fourths of the air occurs in the troposphere, or inner shell.

The Stratosphere

The second layer or intermediate shell of the earth's atmosphere is known as the stratosphere. It extends from the tropopause upward to a height of forty or fifty miles where it ends in a vague level called the stratopause. The temperature at the bottom of the stratosphere varies, but it is always low. Over the Arctic, where the stratosphere lies about four miles above sea level, temperatures of 50° below zero Fahrenheit are recorded. Over the equator, where the stratosphere begins at eleven miles or more above the earth, temperatures of 112° below zero have been observed. Over Chicago, the temperature of the bottom of the stratosphere is about −65°F.

Upward through the stratosphere the temperature lapse rate which characterizes the lower atmosphere does not operate. Man has not as yet ascended very far into the stratosphere, but so far as he has gone, he has found that the temperature does not decrease upward. Indeed, in some instances, it increases slightly with further altitude. How far this isothermal condition (or even actual temperature inversion) continues is not known. It seems logical to assume that toward the top of the stratosphere some rate of temperature decrease is resumed.

Over New York the atmospheric pressure at the bottom of the stratosphere is about seven inches. If one plots the curve of barometric pressure decrease with altitude on a piece of graph paper, the zero point is reached between thirty-five and forty miles. Obviously, therefore, there is no appreciable air pressure at the top of the stratosphere. Approximately one-fourth of the total atmosphere lies in this second shell.

Convection, or the vertical circulation of air, ordinarily does not reach into the stratosphere. Hence, smoke and coarse dust are not carried up into this zone. Water vapor is also not carried up to this level, and hence cumulus clouds are lacking. Some bacteria, spore and volcanic dust do occur. Some carbon dioxide also occurs. Water vapor in small amounts, probably as the result of diffusion, also gets into the stratosphere, and exists as minute frost crystals— manifesting itself as very tenuous cirrus clouds. Storms and storm winds are practically nonexistent. Horizontal winds from east to west, and in lesser degree, from equator to pole, do occur.

The Ionosphere

The ionosphere, or outer shell of the atmosphere has not been, and may never be, explored by man. Most of what we know about it has been gained by inference. It begins at about fifty miles above the geosphere and extends outward for several hundred miles, thinning out gradually to unbelievable rarefaction, and ending in a vague ionopause. The ionosphere probably contains oxygen, nitrogen, hydrogen, helium and other rare gases. All together, these probably amount to less than 1 per cent of the total mass of the atmosphere. Meteors and electrical displays are observed at these high levels. Cosmic dust exists, but it is doubtful whether any moisture, terrestrial dust, or spores ever get to these heights. Beyond the outer edge of the ionosphere, the black-bulb temperature of empty space is more than 400° below zero Fahrenheit—3° Rankine, to be exact. What the temperature within the ionosphere is, we do not know. There is probably a horizontal circulation of air particles in an east to west direction.

Aerial Topography of the Lower Atmosphere

Daily barometric records have been kept at many stations scattered over nearly all parts of the earth. For each station these have been averaged in order to get yearly values for barometric pressure. If these yearly averages are plotted on a world map, they can be connected by lines of equal pressure called isobars, in much the same way that a topographic surveyor draws a contour map in order to show the surface of the land. Indeed, an isobaric map is really a kind of contour map—one that shows the topography of the lower atmosphere.

General World Features

Though this atmospheric topography of the bottom air is invisible to the eye, it is very real nonetheless, as any meteorologist will testify. A meteorologist is an aerial geologist who surveys, maps, studies and interprets this invisible topography. A world map of average yearly atmospheric pressures shows certain major features. Over the Antarctic and Arctic regions lie huge domes of cold, dense, descending air. Midway between these, a great shallow Equatorial Trough straddles the equator and girdles the globe. It contains light, warm, moist, rising air.

Just outside the tropics along either side of the Equatorial Trough lies a long, narrow ridge of cool, clear, dense air. These ridges are not actually continuous around the earth; instead, they are broken into separate segments. That along the northern tropic consists of an elongated Azores Ridge over the central Atlantic and an equally elongated Hawaiian Ridge over the central Pacific. Along and just outside the southern tropic lie the Easter Island Ridge over the south Pacific, the St. Helena Ridge over the south Atlantic, and the Mauritius Ridge over the southern Indian Ocean.

Between these southern ridges and the Antarctic Dome, a very deep trough of cool, moist air runs clear around the world over the polar margins of the southern oceans. This is the Antarctic Trough. There is no continuous trough or valley running around the northern polar margins. Instead, the corresponding region is broken up into two separate oval-shaped basins. Over the northern Atlantic is a huge bowl-like depression known as the Icelandic Basin. It overlies the vast swirl of comparatively warm water carried into the northern Atlantic and Norwegian Sea by the Gulf Stream; this basin contains relatively warm, moist, expanded and usually cloudy air. Over the northern Pacific lies a somewhat similar depression in the atmosphere known as the Aleutian Basin.

Over Eurasia, North America, South Africa, southern South America and Australia, there are extensive, relatively level, aerial plains. They are level, however, only in averaged annual terms. Actually, their atmospheric pressure changes amazingly, from hour to hour and from season to season. At many times they more resemble rugged hill country than they do plains.

Hurricane Regions

Hurricanes are small but violent swirls in the lower atmosphere. In the centers of hurricanes (they are called typhoons in the Orient) the barometric pressure is two or more inches lower than that of the surrounding atmosphere. Since a hurricane is only a hundred miles or so in diameter, this difference means that there is a very steep pressure slope from the outer edge to the center. The surrounding air rushes down the sides of this air basin toward the center. The incoming air forces the warm, light air in the basin to rise. As it rises, the moisture in the air is expanded and cooled. As it cools, it condenses. Rain falls violently over most of the hurricane area. The high wind and heavy rain are often unbelievably destructive.

Storms of the hurricane variety seem to originate on the northern and southern edges of the Equatorial Trough. From there, they move northward or southward as the case may be, usually following a curved parabolic path around the western ends of the high-pressure ridges just outside the tropics.

For instance, one area where such storms originate is the general Caribbean area of the central Atlantic. They first travel northwestward, then northward and finally northeastward around the west end of the Azores Ridge. As they pass off eastward toward the Icelandic Basin, they flatten out and lose their intensity. There are five other similar areas of hurricane activity in the lower atmosphere.

Cyclonic Storm Regions

The great atmospheric plains over the continents are the troublesome areas of the air world. Their pressure is constantly varying. Great domes of cold, dense air overlie each of the polar areas. There is nothing to confine either of these air masses, and hence the outer edge of each of them is an indefinite line called a Polar Front. Sometimes great tongues of cold, heavy air spill southward from the Arctic Dome (or northward from the Antarctic) onto the continents. These tongues get so stretched out that they break off and become roughly oval hills in the atmosphere, known as "anticyclones" or "highs." Their barometric pressure is greatest in the center, but it slopes downward toward the outer margins. The air from the center of the dome flows down the slopes, forming a sort of pinwheel arrangement of winds outward in all directions. Such areas are usually from one to two thousand miles in diameter, and the weather in them is apt to be cool or cold, dry and clear.

The high-pressure ridges just outside the tropics also send tongues of heavy air eastward (and sometimes westward) onto the continents. These often become detached and also form anticyclones. The weather in them is apt to be warmer than that in those of the polar variety.

The areas between anticyclones often fill up with warm, moist air tongues extending up from the Equatorial Trough, or with cool, wet air from the Icelandic and Aleutian Basins or the Antarctic Trough. These warmer tongues of air get pinched off and form roughly oval areas called "cyclones" or "lows." They are about the same size as the anticyclones, but their weather is apt to be warmer, moister and cloudier. Rain and snow often fall in them. Winds blow spirally inward toward the center of a "low" in a reversed pinwheel effect. Many "highs" and "lows" contain *fronts,* the result of a cold air mass pushing against a warm air mass, or a mass of warm air climbing up onto a mass of cold air. Such fronts are invisible, but they are often marked by great air turbulence and masses of cloud. They are really cliffs, precipices, falls and cascades in the atmosphere, to the presence of which any aviator can testify.

Highs and lows are most numerous between latitudes 35° and 55° in either hemisphere. After they are formed, they do not stand still, but begin to move eastward, carried along by the westerly wind circulation. The middle latitudes of the earth thus experience a constant stream of hills and depressions in the atmosphere, all moving eastward. One such procession marches along in the Northern Hemisphere, another in the Southern. Two or three pass a locality within a week's time. One of them requires three or four days to cross the United States and Canada.

Such shifting but invisible topography of the atmosphere is both a blessing and a nuisance. It is a nuisance to aviators and ship navigators, but a blessing to human beings in general. The constantly changing weather which these air masses bring is stimulating to man of the middle latitudes. It makes him energetic. Accordingly, he has made more progress than have his brothers in less changeable portions of the world. For his own protection, however, he has found it necessary to measure the atmosphere each day and publish the data as a daily weather map. This observation enables him to forecast what is coming a few days ahead of time, so that crops, ships, cargoes and land traffic can be protected. Since the development of aviation, hour-by-hour and minute-by-minute weather observations must be made and transmitted far and wide by radio.

The World Wind System

The sun's radiant energy bombards the surface of the earth unequally—most in the tropics and least in the polar regions. The atmosphere is a giant circulating system which equalizes the heat of the tropics and the cold of the polar areas. In the middle troposphere—that is, between three thousand and thirteen thousand feet elevation—cold, heavier air blows from the Arctic and the Antarctic toward the equator. These winds are known as the Upper Trade Winds. As they enter equatorial regions, they push the hot, lighter air upward. This hot air ascends to its ceiling of convection somewhere above thirteen thousand feet and flows back toward the poles as the Anti-Trades.

The winds of the lower part of the troposphere are much more complex than those of the middle and upper parts. They represent air drainage responses to the aerial topography of the lowest one mile of the atmosphere. Air flows off either side of each of the great tropical ridges, off the margins of the polar domes, and down the marginal slopes of the great troughs and basins, as prevailing winds. The air does not flow directly down these slopes as water does down the slopes of the land. Instead, it moves across the isobars at a very acute angle—always toward the right in the Northern Hemisphere and toward the left in the Southern.

The North Atlantic region illustrates this airflow excellently (see below). It is overlain, from north to south, by the Arctic Dome, the Icelandic Basin, the Azores Ridges and the Equatorial Trough. Air flowing off the Arctic Dome and down the northern slope of the Icelandic Basin creates the Northeast Polar Winds. Air flowing off the north slope of the Azores Ridge and down the southern slope of the

Icelandic Basin gives rise to the Prevailing Southwesterly Winds. Air draining down the southern slope of the Azores Ridge and into the Equatorial Trough produces the Northeast Trade Winds. The central parts of these areas are marked by calms or light, variable winds. Comparable conditions exist over all the oceans; over the lands, extremely fluctuating cyclonic and anticyclonic conditions obtain. All these features, combined, produce a lower-atmospheric circulation pattern that is known as the world

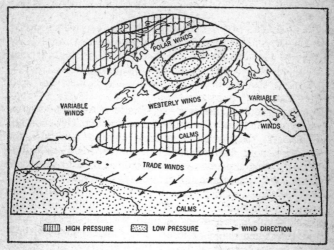

The prevailing winds of the North Atlantic

wind system. An earth with its surface all water or all land would exhibit a perfect and regular pattern of parallel belts of winds and strips of calms extending around it in an east-west direction. Our earth being what it is, the actual wind system is only an approximation of such a pattern.

Long ago the Norse Vikings discovered Iceland, Greenland and the North American continent by way of the Northeast Polar Winds. On their return trips to northern Europe they employed the Westerly Winds. Much later Columbus discovered America via the Northeast Trade Winds and returned via the Westerlies. Today transatlantic planes from North America to Europe follow these same Westerlies. Returning to America, they follow the Northeast Polar Winds. Eventually, as intercontinental stratosphere flying develops, planes will fly over the polar dome directly from Europe to America and back. In these latitudes the stratosphere descends to four miles or less, and hence is easily accessible. Storms, cloudiness, adverse winds and dangerous icing conditions will thus be avoided, and much greater safety assured. In the future, the atmospheric pattern will become more and more important as an element in man's environment.

Crumbling Rocks

By Raymond E. Janssen

Probably there is nothing in Nature more grand and imposing than a lofty mountain, its towering peak snow-capped and glistening like a diadem in the sunlight, its enormous bulk fashioned from massive, solid rock. By contrast, nothing else on earth seems to be more firm and stable. . . . There are numerous sayings to the effect that something is "as old as the hills" or "as hard as a rock."

On the other hand, if one will pause to think a moment, it is self-evident that even the hardest rocks are subject to breakdown and decay. There are various examples of this on every hand. Inscriptions on old tombstones are slowly obliterated after many decades; surfaces of old stone edifices crumble away; stone steps of public buildings are gradually hollowed out by the constant tread of leather soles. Along country roads where the highway has been cut through rock strata, the stone soon loses its appearance of freshness, pitted surfaces develop, and pieces of rock slough off to collect in heaps at the base. If changes such as these occur within a few years or decades, infinitely greater ones must take place over periods of thousands or millions of years.

Detailed study of such phenomena has shown that over long periods of time all rocks exposed at the earth's surface are readily altered. For the most part, these changes are accomplished, directly or indirectly, by the action of the atmosphere and precipitation and hence are appropriately termed rock-weathering. Depending upon the prevailing weather and climate and kind of rock in any given region, the alteration process may be dominantly chemical, mechanical or a combination of both. In humid regions the rock surfaces become dull and stained, crumbly and pitted, as a result of chemical action of the moisture upon the minerals comprising the rocks, causing the latter literally to decay or decompose. It is this same process that causes old tin cans or the unpainted surface of bridges and other structures to flake off in the form of rust. In arid regions, on the other hand, the surfaces of the rocks may remain reasonably fresh, but cracks and fissures appear, and thin slivers and shells break away from the surfaces. Because here the air is relatively dry, the process is essentially mechanical in nature. Both processes, however, are forms of rock-weathering.

As a result of either of these processes or both of them, solid and firm rock ultimately crumbles into small pieces, grains and dust. If the exposed rock forms the side of a cliff, steep valley or mountain side, the weathered and loosened fragments slide or creep downgrade to build up heaps of debris, called talus, at the base of the parent rock mass. In some mountainous regions such heaps of slide-rock finally become so great as to bury the whole mountain side. If the bedrock is only gently inclined or essentially horizontal, the small fragments remain scattered on the surface, eventually weathering into smaller and smaller particles to form the mantle of soil that characteristically covers extensive areas of the earth's surface. In any region where soil lies on the surface, observation shows that with depth it grades downward into coarser and coarser fragments until the parent bedrock is reached. Such depths may, in various regions, be a matter of only a few inches or of hundreds of feet.

Because this mantle of broken rock and soil consists of relatively small particles, it is readily carried away by such mechanical forces as wind, running water or ice, giving rise to the familiar phenomenon known as erosion. Thus rock-weathering and erosion operate hand in hand to break down the solid rock and carry it away bit by bit to lower levels and finally to the sea. Through these combined processes, operating continuously through the ages, mountains are worn low and continental areas of past times have been literally washed away. Geologically, such events are of little moment in themselves because new lands and new mountains have continually been rebuilt or re-elevated from time to time to take the place of those that have been destroyed. From the human viewpoint, however, rock-weathering and the resulting erosion are of tremendous consequence, particularly where agriculture and related industries depend upon the use of the soil.

In nature, rock-weathering and erosion more or less keep pace with each other, thereby insuring retention of the soil mantle in regions where it has been developed. Here, ground water and air, penetrating downward through the interspaces of the soil, slowly weather the bedrock beneath, breaking it into smaller particles, even though the rock is blanketed by many feet of mantle. If the topsoil is not carried away too fast, this slow weathering of the rock beneath continues in pace with the normal erosion of the soil above. Thus, under normal conditions in most areas of the world, the soil mantle, as a unit, would remain essentially static were it not for improper agricultural practices that permit erosion to operate faster than new soil can be formed by weathering. If researchers in rock-weathering could discover practical means whereby natural weathering could be greatly speeded, some of our serious erosion problems might be solved.

Theoretically, rock-weathering is considered by geologists as being merely the process whereby massive rock is disintegrated or decomposed into smaller and finer particles, regardless of the manner in which it is accomplished. Erosion, on the other hand, involves the removal of these particles from their original sites to any other location, their ultimate destination usually being the sea. From a practical standpoint, however, it is not always possible to differentiate clearly between weathering and erosion, since the two are so interrelated that they usually aid and abet each other. This is particularly true where so-called mechanical weathering appears to be the dominant factor. Because rock is a relatively poor conductor of heat, the sun's rays cause exposed surfaces to become heated and expanded more than the interior, resulting in strains that weaken the rock. At night there may be a reversal of this condition, the rock surfaces losing their heat and becoming colder than the inside. Such expansions are characteristic of desert and semiarid regions where temperatures may be quite high in the daytime and correspondingly low at night. As a result of these expansions and contractions over long periods, the rock finally yields by shelling off its outer layer. As fresh surfaces are exposed, the process is repeated. Although such action may be primarily mechanical, it is aided by chemical reactions when small amounts of moisture enter the cracks developed in this way and further the decomposition of the mineral matter comprising the rock. The loose shells of rock which thus fall away from the parent mass are not completely weathered, however, and may lie for many years on the ground before they are finally broken into particles small enough to be picked up by erosion agents and carried away. The great structure known as Half Dome, in Yosemite National Park, exhibits this form of weathering in enormous degree.

Closely related to the foregoing process is that wherein water enters the crevices and pores of rocks and becomes frozen when the temperature drops. The expansion of the ice may exert sufficient pressure to pry the rocks apart, and, with alternate periods of thawing and freezing, great chunks of rock may be loosened and fall away from the main rock mass. In the same way, the roots of trees penetrating down into small rock fissures may exert sufficient force while growing to lift and pry away large slabs of rock. In addition, the mere difference in physical characteristics of alternating layers of rock may contribute to their disruption. Common examples of this may be seen wherever there are overhanging cliffs. Here soft, or more easily weathered, strata of rocks are topped by more resistant layers. The former, in weathering, are cut back under the overlying layers, eventually contributing to the downfall of the harder layers.

Theoretically, mechanical weathering can be distinguished from chemical weathering. The former is simply the breakdown of the parent rock mass into smaller pieces of varying size and shape, enabling them to be moved by

HOW CAVERNS ARE FORMED

1. Limestone is laid down under the sea

2. The limestone is lifted by crustal movement

3. Water seeping through cracks dissolves the rock

4. Forming caverns. All this happens in rocks saturated with water

5. Water table falls, emptying cavern and allowing stalactites to form

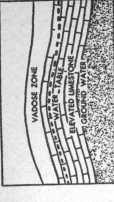

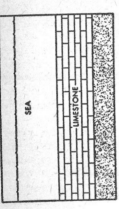

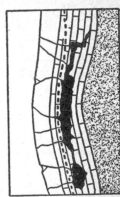

gravity or by eroding agents. Chemical weathering, however, involves an actual chemical change in the composition of the minerals comprising the rocks. Air and water, particularly if combined with carbonic acid from decaying vegetation, are powerful decomposers of rock materials; hence these agents literally tend to eat away the rock minerals. If any part of the mineral constituents of a rock mass is thus decayed away, the remaining structure may become so porous and weakened as to be much more easily attacked by mechanical processes. Only under very limited conditions are rocks completely weathered solely by one or the other means. Usually both forces operate together. It can be readily understood that when rocks are disintegrated by mechanical means, the smaller fragments expose a greater total surface area to the attack of chemical agents, permitting the latter to perform their work more effectively. And this, in turn, may quicken further mechanical breakdown. Some types of rocks and minerals, such as limestone, marble, salt and gypsum, are quite susceptible to chemical attack; whereas others, such as shale, quartzite and many volcanic rocks, are not and are therefore broken down principally by mechanical means.

Having been weathered, all rock particles are subject to transport, technically called erosion, whereby they are removed to other locations and ultimately to the sea. Depending upon the region, the erosion agents are wind, ice or water. Operating most effectively in arid regions, the wind picks up the smaller weathered particles, such as dust and fine sand grains, often carrying them great distances before dropping them again. During the exceptionally dry periods of 1934–36, enormous dust storms, originating in the Great Plains of the United States, swept eastward across the continent. At Chicago, Detroit and farther east, these storms were of such intensity as to black out the sun at midday. In some instances, the storms raced onward over the Atlantic, and sailors on ships at sea actually swept the dust of our Western prairies from their decks.

The wind, as an erosion agent, may also do much weathering. The loose sand grains, as they are blown along, may be hurled against projecting masses of rock with such force as to abrade, or wear away, their surfaces by a natural sandblast. Since the wind usually cannot lift sand grains very high from the ground, most of the sandblasting action occurs within a few feet of the ground. This results in undercutting of the rocks to produce many curious rock formations, such as "toadstool rocks," balanced rocks and oval caves in cliff sides. Oftentimes telephone poles and fence posts are cut off near the ground line by such sandblasting.

Running water, because of its almost universal distribution, is generally conceded to be the most important erosive agent. Most readily understood of all geologic processes is the part that surface streams play in land erosion by carrying away in suspension most of the weathered products of their drainage areas. In order to study the transporting power of streams, gauging stations are maintained near the mouths of many large rivers. In this way it has been determined that the Mississippi River normally carries more than a million tons of sediment daily to the Gulf of Mexico. Less well known, however, is the fact that these suspended particles of sediment may themselves act as further agents of weathering, as do the wind-carried particles. While being swirled along in the streams, the grains strike against the sides and the bedrock of the stream channels, grinding off additional particles of rock. It is also recognized that streams may transport stones that are too large and heavy for them to carry by suspension. They do this simply by rolling or buffeting them along their beds. Because of their greater gradients, tiny mountain streams may do this even more effectively than large, sluggish rivers. Frequently such stones roll into irregular depressions of the stream bed. If they are too heavy to roll out of the depression again, they may be swirled around and around in it, resulting in the grinding out of deep hollows, termed potholes. A long series of these may be spaced so close together as to coalesce, or cut into one another, eventually lowering the stream bed.

Any stream, whether it be on the surface or underground, and depending upon the kind of rock over or through which it is flowing, may also dissolve the rock. This is most pronounced where subsurface streams flow through crevices in limestone or other soluble types of rocks. This is, of course, a chemical action wherein the rock is weathered and carried away immediately in solution. All our large and beautiful caverns, such as Carlsbad, Mammoth and Luray, were hollowed out by extended enlargement of cracks in the limestone by this dissolving power of running water.

Even nonflowing waters, such as the sea itself, are powerful weathering and eroding agents along the shores where they come into direct contact with the land. Rocky sea cliffs are battered to pieces by the onslaught of the waves. This is accomplished largely by the air that occupies the crevices in the rocks becoming compressed when the waves slap against it. The compressed air then tends to spread the rocks apart, eventually weakening them to the crumbling point. The broken rocks fall to the beach, where the waves pound them into fragments small enough to be carried out to sea by the undertow and longshore currents.

In some respects, ice may be the most powerful eroding agent of all, particularly in regions where it occurs as enormous glaciers. Because of its rigidity, ice offers greater resistance than does either water or wind; therefore, when glacial ice moves over rock surfaces it may actually gouge out rocks that neither wind nor water could easily reach. The rock fragments thus gouged out may then become frozen in the bottom of the glacier and abrade the surfaces over which they move. In this way the glacier acts like a gigantic piece of sandpaper, grinding down the lands over which it passes. Also, in contrast to flowing water, which receives its momentum from gravity, glaciers may actually move uphill, wearing off the tops of hills and mountains as they ride up and over them. The method of uphill movement of ice may be visualized by likening a glacier to a string of railroad cars that are being pushed upgrade by a locomotive. The glacial ice accumulates from compacted snow that has fallen in the region of greatest precipitation. After a sufficient thickness of ice has thus been mounded up (usually several hundred to a thousand feet or more), it begins to move under its own weight, continuing to move thereafter as long as snow continues to be added at the accumulation point. The pressure thus created may cause the extremities of the glacier to move uphill if any elevations stand in its path. Thus the forward end of a glacier may act like a gigantic plow as it is shoved along.

Valley glaciers, those long, narrow rivers of ice that characteristically move down the sides of high mountains, are enormous carriers of rock debris. As they slowly wind their way down through the valleys, the flowing ice tends to conform to the valley shapes; but because the ice is nevertheless rigid, it cuts away at the sides and bottoms of the valleys, ever widening and deepening them by abrasion against the rock. As the valleys are cut wider and deeper, the upper parts of the valley walls may be left so poorly supported that slides and avalanches catapult down upon the glaciers from overhead. This material, often consisting of rocks and boulders of immense size, then rides along on top of the glaciers as though on great sleds. In this way rocks larger than houses can be carried along by the moving ice, a feat impossible for wind or water to accomplish.

Since, by definition, rock-weathering is the process of disintegrating or decomposing the rock into smaller pieces, and erosion is that of carrying these particles away, it should follow that the two processes are distinct in themselves. Yet, when one observes these activities taking place, it is virtually impossible to draw sharp lines between them. At what point do wind, water and ice cease to break rock and, thereafter, merely transport it? The two processes may actually work simultaneously, and further weathering may continue while the fragments are being transported. Only in the case of chemical weathering, wherein the rock material is completely dissolved and combined with the moving water, does weathering cease before final deposition in the sea. It is also true that neither weathering nor erosion could long continue without the other. Without weathering there would be no rock particles to be transported; and without erosion the weathered fragments would accumulate to such depths that the agents of weathering could not penetrate beneath the debris, and further weathering would cease. We have only to study the surface of our moon in order to visualize a condition wherein weathering and erosion do not occur. Because there is no atmosphere and no water on the moon, its surface remains unchanged except for the impact of falling meteors.

The profound effects resulting from the combined action of weathering and erosion account for nearly all the geologic changes that occur on the surface of the earth. The only exceptions are the processes of volcanism, faulting and regional uplift, wherein new lands may be built and old ones shifted in position. . . .

To weathering and erosion, then, may be attributed nearly all those natural features of the earth considered beautiful in the eyes of man: the towering mountains, peaceful valleys, sweeping hills, broad plains and dashing waterfalls. There are few individuals who can look upon beautiful scenery without experiencing some inward feeling of emotion at the wonders displayed before them. Such vistas may at first appear mysterious and meaningless but, upon study and contemplation, may be read like the pages of a book. It is the mighty history of an ever changing earth wherein rock piled on rock is slowly crumbled away, only to be rebuilt from the products of its own destruction into new rocks of some succeeding age. The words of the prophet, written several millennia ago, still ring with truth:

> The everlasting mountains were scattered, the perpetual hills did bow: his ways are everlasting.—Hab. 3:6.

The Erosion Cycle
By Herdman F. Cleland

The terms *youth, maturity,* and *old age* are used to express the characteristics of valleys, and are helpful since they are as descriptive of them as the same terms applied to human beings. "They have reference not so much to the length of their history in years as to the amount of work which streams have accomplished in comparison with what they have before them."

Youth

Young valleys are V-shaped, with steep sides, and are occupied by rapid streams unless the land is low. Since they have had but a short life, rapids and waterfalls are often numerous; the divides are wide and ill-drained, as the frequent occurrence of marshes and lakes usually indicates. The Grand Canyon of the Colorado, the steep gorge of the Niagara River, and all narrow, steep-sided, or V-shaped valleys are in youth. A *region* is said to be youthful when sufficient time has not elapsed for streams thoroughly to dissect and drain it; in other words, *the streams have the larger part of their task before them*. The Red River Valley of North Dakota and Minnesota is such a region, since it has not long been subjected to stream erosion. It was formerly the site of a lake whose bed was covered evenly with sediment. After the lake was drained the bed was exposed to erosion, and a drainage system was developed whose stream courses were determined by the inequalities of the bottom. Later in its history new tributaries will erode side valleys, the main valleys will be widened, and a mature topography will result.

Maturity

A mature valley is deep, but has flaring sides and gently rounded upper slopes. A region in full maturity is in decided contrast to a youthful region. Instead of a few tributaries and consequently wide divides, the land is thoroughly dissected by valleys, the divides are narrow, the valley sides are less steep than in youth, and the streams are accomplishing their greatest work both in erosion and transportation. In such a region the rainfall runs almost immediately into the streams; lakes have practically disappeared, having been drained by the cutting down of their outlets or filled by stream sediment and organic matter. In this state the relief is greatest, and arable land is at a minimum; roads are difficult and must follow either the valleys or the narrow divides, and the inhabitants are isolated. There are many such regions in the United States; for example, large portions of West Virginia, southeastern Ohio, eastern Kentucky and Tennessee are in maturity. As a rule a master stream reaches maturity earlier than its tributaries, and in its lower course earlier than in its upper course. A region in maturity may be traversed by a stream which flows through a broad, *old* valley, and a youthful region may be traversed by a mature stream.

Old Age

Continued erosion will gradually cut down the valley sides to gentle slopes, lower the divides, and thus tend to reduce the surface to an undulating plain. The sluggish streams will meander in wide valleys. The region is then in *old age.* An absolute plain may, perhaps, never be reached, since elevations will be left here and there because of some favoring condition, such as (1) hardness of rock or (2) a favoring position with reference to the drainage of the plain. Such hills or mountains rising above the general level of the surface are called *monadnocks,* from a mountain of that type in New Hampshire. Portions of Kansas have passed through youth and maturity and are now in the stage of old age.

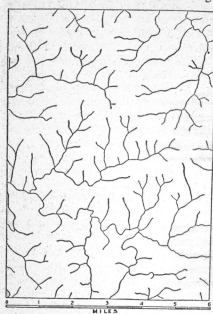

Map showing the stream courses in a mature region

The time required for the production of a base-leveled condition or for "peneplana-

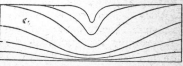

Diagram showing the profile of young, mature, and old valleys

tion" is called the *cycle of erosion.* It will take, perhaps, one hundred thousand times as long to pass from maturity to old age as from youth to maturity. It will be seen from the above that age of a region is not recorded in years but in the work accomplished or to be accomplished.

Effect of Elevation and Depression on Streams

If a region is elevated after it has been reduced to base level (peneplain), the streams will be quickened and will again be enabled to deepen their valleys. If the streams meandered on the peneplains, they may intrench themselves in their old courses until they flow through deep, meandering rock gorges. When a stream has thus intrenched its meanders, the evidence is strong that it has been rejuvenated. Many examples of intrenched meanders are to be seen in Europe and in the United States. In the latter, Pennsylvania, Kentucky and Utah furnish excellent and striking examples. The great natural bridges of Utah, one of which has a height of three hundred and five feet and a span of two hundred and seventy-three feet, were formed by the perforation of the necks of intrenched meanders, as was also that of the Ardèche River, France.

If a region is uplifted before the erosion cycle is completed, the rivers will deepen their courses, leaving their former broad flood plains standing as terraces or "benches." A section of such a valley will show a valley within a valley. If a region is more elevated near the ocean than further inland, the upper courses of the streams will be "ponded," unless they are able to deepen their valleys as rapidly as the land is elevated. This differential movement of the earth's surface is called *warping*. Streams which hold their courses in spite of differential elevations are called antecedent streams.

If a region underlain by tilted rocks which vary in composition, some resisting erosion more than others, is reduced to base level and then raised, the subsequent erosion is such as to give certain proof of its earlier history. An interesting example, in which, however, the river encountered granite rather than tilted rock, is found in the history of the Gunnison River in Colorado. When the Rocky Mountains were being uplifted to their present position, the streams which now drain them began to cut their valleys. Among them the Gunnison River followed along the depression of the plateau and began to deepen its bed. Its course happened to lie over a great mass of granite, buried beneath softer strata. The river, having a steep gradient, rapidly cut its way through the soft surface rocks and finally encountered the granite. Since its valley was already deep when this occurred, it was unable to turn aside from the hard rock and continued to cut its way through it until the picturesque Black Canyon, more than two thousand feet deep, was excavated. The Uncompahgre River, which joins the Gunnison after flowing in approximately the same direction for some distance, was born at the same time. It has flowed, however, over soft material which could be readily eroded, and has been able to excavate a valley several miles in width which in one place is separated from the narrow Black Canyon by a narrow ridge of granite.

If a region is depressed, the velocity of the streams will be lessened, and the condition of old age will be hastened. Drowned river valleys such as the Delaware, the St. Lawrence and Chesapeake Bay are the result of the sinking of the land in the lower courses of the rivers.

The Mississippi
By Mark Twain

The Mississippi is well worth reading about. It is not a commonplace river, but on the contrary is in all ways remarkable. Considering the Missouri its main branch, it is the longest river in the world—four thousand, three hundred miles. It seems safe to say that it is also the crookedest river in the world, since in one part of its journey it uses up one thousand, three hundred miles to cover the same ground that the crow would fly over in six hundred and seventy-five. It discharges three times as much water as the St. Lawrence, twenty-five times as much as the Rhine and three hundred and thirty-eight times as much as the Thames. No other river has so vast a drainage basin; it draws its water supply from twenty-eight states and territories; from Delaware, on the Atlantic seaboard, and from all the country between that and Idaho on the Pacific slope—a spread of 45° of longitude. The Mississippi receives and carries to the Gulf water from fifty-four subordinate rivers that are navigable by steamboats, and from some hundreds that are navigable by flats and keels. The area of its drainage basin is as great as the combined areas of England, Wales, Scotland, Ireland, France, Spain, Portugal, Germany, Austria, Italy and Turkey; and almost all this wide region is fertile; the Mississippi valley, proper, is exceptionally so.

It is a remarkable river in this: that instead of widening toward its mouth, it grows narrower; grows narrower and deeper. From the junction of the Ohio to a point halfway down to the sea, the width averages a mile in high water; thence to the sea the width steadily diminishes, until, at the "Passes," above the mouth, it is but little over half a mile. At the junction of the Ohio the Mississippi's depth is eighty-seven feet; the depth increases gradually, reaching one hundred and twenty-nine just above the mouth.

The difference in rise and fall is also remarkable—not in the upper but in the lower river. The rise is tolerably uniform down to Natchez (three hundred and sixty miles above the mouth)—about fifty feet. But at Bayou La Fourche the river rises only twenty-four feet; at New Orleans only fifteen, and just above the mouth only two and one-half.

An article in the *New Orleans Times-Democrat,* based upon reports of able engineers, states that the river annually empties four hundred and six million tons of mud into the Gulf of Mexico—which brings to mind Captain Marryat's rude name for the Mississippi—"the Great Sewer." This mud, solidified, would make a mass a mile square and two hundred and forty-one feet high.

The mud deposit gradually extends the land—but only gradually; it has extended it not quite a third of a mile in the two hundred years which have elapsed since the river took its place in history. The belief of the scientific people is that the mouth used to be at Baton Rouge, where the hills cease, and that the two hundred miles of land between there and the Gulf was built by the river. This gives us the age of that piece of country, without any trouble at all—one hundred and twenty thousand years. Yet it is much the youthfulest batch of country that lies around there anywhere.

The Mississippi is remarkable in still another way—its disposition to make prodigious jumps by cutting through narrow necks of land, and thus straightening and shortening itself. More than once it has shortened itself thirty miles at a single jump! These cut-offs have had curious effects: they have thrown several river towns out into the rural districts, and built up sand bars and forests in front of them. The town of Delta used to be three miles below Vicksburg; a recent cut-off has radically changed the position, and Delta is now *two miles above* Vicksburg.

Both of these river towns have been retired to the country by that cut-off. A cut-off plays havoc with boundary lines and jurisdictions; for instance, a man is living in the State of Mississippi today, a cut-off occurs tonight, and tomorrow the man finds himself and his land over on the other side of the river, within the boundaries and subject to the laws of the State of Louisiana! Such a thing, happening in the upper river in the old times, could have transferred a slave from Missouri to Illinois and made a free man of him.

The Mississippi does not alter its locality by cut-offs alone: it is always changing its habitat *bodily*—is always moving bodily *sidewise*. At Hard Times, Louisiana, the river is two miles west of the region it used to occupy. As a result, the original *site* of that settlement is not now in Louisiana at all, but on the other side of the river, in the State of Mississippi. *Nearly the whole of that one thousand, three hundred miles of old Mississippi River which La Salle floated down in his canoes, two hundred years ago, is good solid dry ground now.* The river lies to the right of it, in places, and to the left of it in other places.

Although the Mississippi's mud builds land but slowly, down at the mouth, where the Gulf's billows interfere with its work, it builds fast enough in better protected regions higher up; for instance, Prophet's Island contained one thousand, five hundred acres of land thirty years ago; since then the river has added seven hundred acres to it. . . .

These dry details are of importance in one particular. They give me an opportunity of introducing one of the Mississippi's oddest peculiarities—that of shortening its length from time to time. If you will throw a long, pliant apple paring over your shoulder, it will pretty fairly shape itself into an average section of the Mississippi River; that is, the nine or ten hundred miles stretching from Cairo, Illinois, southward to New Orleans, the same being wonderfully crooked, with a brief straight bit here and there at wide intervals. The two-hundred-mile stretch from Cairo northward to the St. Louis is by no means so crooked, that being a rocky country which the river cannot cut much.

The water cuts the alluvial banks of the "lower" river into deep horseshoe curves, so deep, indeed, that in some places if you were to get ashore at one extremity of the horseshoe and walk across the neck, half or three-quarters of a mile, you could sit down and rest a couple of hours while your steamer was coming around the long elbow at a speed of ten miles an hour to take you on board again. When the river is rising fast, some scoundrel whose plantation is back in the country, and therefore of inferior value, has only to watch his chance, cut a little gutter across the narrow neck of land some dark night, and turn the water into it, and in a wonderfully short time a miracle has happened; to wit, the whole Mississippi has taken possession of that little ditch, and placed the countryman's plantation on its bank (quadrupling its value), and that other party's formerly valuable plantation finds itself away out yonder on a big island; the old watercourse around it will soon shoal up, boats cannot approach within ten miles of it, and down goes its value to a fourth of its former worth. Watches are kept on those narrow necks at needful times, and if a man happens to be caught cutting a ditch across them, the chances are all against his ever having another opportunity to cut a ditch.

Pray observe some of the effects of this ditching business. Once there was a neck opposite Port Hudson, Louisiana, which was only half a mile across in its narrowest place. You could walk across there in fifteen minutes; but if you made the journey around the cape on a raft, you traveled thirty-five miles to accomplish the same thing. In 1722 the river darted through that neck, deserted its old bed, and thus shortened itself thirty-five miles. In the same way it shortened itself twenty-five miles at Black Hawk Point in 1699. Below Red River Landing, Raccourci cut-off was made (forty or fifty years ago, I think). This shortened the river twenty-eight miles. In our day, if you travel by river from the southernmost of these three cut-offs to the northernmost, you go only seventy miles. To do the same thing a hundred and seventy-six years ago, one had to go a hundred and fifty-eight miles—a shortening of eighty-eight miles in that trifling distance. At some forgotten time in the past, cut-offs were made above Vidalia, Louisiana, at Island 92, at Island 84, and at Hale's Point. These shortened the river, in the aggregate, seventy-seven miles.

Since my own day on the Mississippi, cut-offs have been made at Hurricane Island, at Island 100, at Napoleon, Arkansas, at Walnut Bend and at Council Bend. These shortened the river, in the aggregate, sixty-seven miles. In my own time a cut-off was made at American Bend, which shortened the river ten miles or more.

Therefore the Mississippi between Cairo and New Orleans was twelve hundred and fifteen miles long one hundred and seventy-six years ago. It was eleven hundred and eighty after the cut-off of 1722. It was one thousand and forty after the American Bend cut-off. It has lost sixty-seven miles since. Consequently, its length is only nine hundred and seventy-three miles at present.

Now, if I wanted to be one of those ponderous scientific people, and "let on" to prove what had occurred in the remote past by what had occurred in a given time in the recent past, or what will occur in the far future by what has occurred in late years, what an opportunity is here! Geology never had such a chance, nor such exact data to argue from! Nor "development of species," either! Glacial epochs are great things, but they are vague—vague. Please observe:

In the space of one hundred and seventy-six years the lower Mississippi has shortened itself two hundred and forty-two miles. That is an average of a trifle over one mile and a third per year. Therefore, any calm person, who is not blind or idiotic, can see that in the Old Oölitic Silurian Period, just a million years ago next November, the lower Mississippi River was upward of one million, three hundred thousand miles long, and stuck out over the Gulf of Mexico like a fishing rod. And by the same token any person can see that seven hundred and forty-two years from now the lower Mississippi will be only a mile and three-quarters long, and Cairo and New Orleans will have joined their streets together, and be plodding comfortably along under a single mayor and a mutual board of aldermen. There is something fascinating about science. One gets such wholesale returns of conjecture out of such a trifling investment of fact.

Glaciers

By Richard Foster Flint

One day in the summer of 1937, I went over the side of an exploration ship in an iceberg-dotted fiord of East Greenland and, in a spirit of scientific inquiry, rowed toward a large "dirty" berg. Icebergs come from glaciers that have flowed down to tidewater; the ends of the glaciers break off or are buoyed up and then float away. A "dirty" berg is one with pieces of rock and earth embedded in it. Usually such a berg comes from the very base or sole of the glacier—the part that has been in contact with the ground beneath it during its long, slow-flowing journey to the seacoast.

I wanted to find out what kinds of rocks and minerals constitute the ground beneath all that glacial ice in the interior of Greenland—ice with an area of six hundred and thirty-seven thousand square miles. There is no way to get to the subglacial surface. The best one can do is to let the glacier tear off, transport and deliver what it will, and to look hopefully at what is offered. On that particular day in 1937, I found nothing noteworthy, but the possibilities are dramatic. Who knows what mineral wealth may be hidden beneath the six hundred and thirty-seven thousand square miles of the Greenland Ice Sheet, or beneath the five million square miles of ice that cover the Antarctic Continent? These ice sheets are the world's two largest glaciers.

Not many Americans have seen a glacier at close range, simply because there aren't many glaciers in the United States and because those we have are tucked away in fairly high, inaccessible places. Still, the residents of such western cities as Seattle and Portland live within sight of glaciers. To the large number of Swiss citizens who live in farmhouses within a short walk of one or another of the more than twelve hundred glaciers in the Alps, a glacier is an everyday thing, hardly worth noticing. But to most of us it is an object of considerable curiosity.

A glacier is nothing more than snow compacted into ice, spreading outward and flowing downward from the places (usually high) where the snow accumulated. What makes a glacier move is roughly the same thing that makes batter spread outward when it is poured onto a griddle. To be sure, batter is a liquid—a rather stiff liquid—whereas ice is a solid. But when it is hard pressed by the great weight of more ice on top of it, it becomes a very weak solid; it yields easily and flows almost as if it were a liquid. On a flat surface, it spreads out and forms an ice sheet having the pancake form of the spread-out batter. On an irregular surface, ice flows down the steepest path it can find. Because snow is usually thicker and more persistent on mountains than on plains, the resulting ice takes the form of the mountain valleys down which it flows, thus forming the tonguelike valley glaciers that we associate with most cold mountain regions. Valley glaciers are the glacial counterparts of the streams of water that course downward through mountain valleys in milder climates.

How thick does a pile of snow have to be in order to flow and become a glacier? Only about one hundred to two hundred feet. At that thickness, most of the snow will have become ice. Scientists on sledge expeditions across large ice sheets have found, by digging pits into the surface, that the snow is layered. Each layer represents one year's accumulation, and each is a little more dense than the layer above it. Layer by layer the snow packs down, settles and recrystallizes. Because of these changes, the snow is transformed, as we follow it downward, into granular névé ("buckshot snow") and finally into solid ice. The weight of a few score feet of this ice is enough to overcome the rather feeble strength of the ice still farther beneath. As a result, the ice underneath moves slowly outward in much the same way as will toothpaste or vaseline gently squeezed out of an opened tube laid on a table.

In the uppermost one hundred to two hundred feet of the glacier's thickness, the weight is not great enough to produce this effect, so the ice there remains rigid and brittle. It is somewhat like the rigid shell on the back of a turtle, which is carried along by the mobile animal "underneath" it.

Like all brittle and rigid substances, this upper shell of ice will crack when subjected to great stress. This happens when the following ice moves over a buried hill or down a sudden steepening of the slope of the glacier's rocky floor. The resulting cracks, or *crevasses,* are very numer-

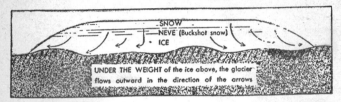

UNDER THE WEIGHT of the ice above, the glacier flows outward in the direction of the arrows

ous in some places. They extend one hundred to two hundred feet down into the glacier but no farther, for below this depth the pressure is great enough to close them up and keep them closed.

Crevasses are a tremendous hindrance to travel over the surface of a glacier. In the winter, they are likely to become bridged by drifting snow, which obliterates the

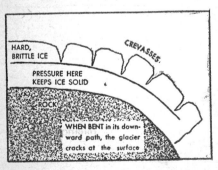

HARD, BRITTLE ICE

CREVASSES

PRESSURE HERE KEEPS ICE SOLID

ROCK

WHEN BENT in its downward path, the glacier cracks at the surface

great gaping cracks many feet in width. Often the bridges will support the weight of a man or a sledge, but sometimes they collapse, causing tragic disasters.

In 1820, three climbers on a valley glacier on Mont Blanc, in the French Alps, were overwhelmed by a snow avalanche, swept into a crevasse, and lost. From measurements of the glacier's rate of flow, it was predicted that the bodies of the unfortunate climbers would reach the lower end of the glacier about forty years after the accident. The prediction proved accurate. Beginning in 1861, after the lapse of forty-one years, their heads, other parts of their bodies and their clothing and equipment were delivered up, having traveled at an average rate of two hundred twenty-five feet per year. The shearing stresses involved in the flow of the ice had gradually dismembered the bodies.

The rate of flow of this Mont Blanc glacier, two hundred twenty-five feet per year, is a typical figure for a valley glacier. Average figures mean little, because variable slopes, temperatures and thicknesses cause great variations between one glacier and another and even between different parts of the same glacier.

A record rate of flow was established by the Black Rapids Glacier, in the interior of Alaska. Ten miles long in 1936, this tongue of ice suddenly began to move rapidly, increasing its length to thirteen miles within less than five months. During this time its rate of flow exceeded one hundred fifteen feet per day. The burst of speed, however, soon died down. Investigating geologists decided it was brought about by a previous succession of winters that had been marked by unusually heavy snowfall. Today the Black Rapids Glacier, after its spectacular effort, is melting and shrinking away.

A similar burst of speed by an Alaskan valley glacier became a serious threat to a $1.5 million railroad bridge. This bridge, key link in the $20 million Copper River and Northwestern Railway, was built in 1909 and 1910 at the only practicable crossing of the river—a point well below the end, or terminus, of the Childs Glacier. The terminus was a formidable cliff of ice three hundred feet high and three miles wide, but its presence caused no great concern, because for many years the cliff had been nearly stationary. Melting had struck a balance with the slow forward flow of the glacier. Then, before the bridge was completed, the ice cliff suddenly began to edge forward, as if aroused by the trespass upon its domain. By the summer of 1911, it had crept down to within fifteen hundred feet of the bridge and towered above it. Its rate of advance had touched a high point of eight feet per day.

The bridge engineers were helpless to avert the impending catastrophe. Then, late in 1911, the cliff suddenly faltered, stopped and began to recede; it has been receding ever since. The cause of the abrupt change is not known. The best explanation seems to be that earthquakes in 1899 and 1900 caused the avalanching of a vast quantity of snow and ice onto the upstream part of the glacier. This unusual increment was added to by a succession of very snowy winters between 1902 and 1909. The glacier was made thicker, and its rate of flow increased correspondingly. The wave of increased flow traveled down the length of the glacier somewhat as the high point of a flood travels down the length of a river.

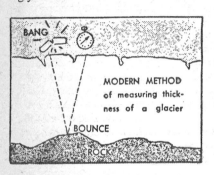

MODERN METHOD of measuring thickness of a glacier

One reason why most valley glaciers do not flow rapidly is because they are not very thick. Many small valley glaciers are probably no more than two or three hundred feet in thickness, and most of the big ones are probably less than a thousand feet. For most glaciers these figures are only estimates, as very few have actually been measured. The method of measurement is the same as one used by oil geologists to determine thicknesses of rock layers buried beneath the surface. It consists of starting a little earthquake, with a charge of blasting powder, at the surface of the glacier. The earthquake waves pass down through the ice, are reflected by the rock floor beneath, and return to the surface, where they are recorded by special instruments that accurately time the round trip of the waves through the glacier. The approximate rate of travel through ice being known, the ice thickness can then be computed.

This method was used on the Greenland Ice Sheet by a small group of scientists. These men, with dogs and sledges, braved much hardship in hauling their equipment hundreds of miles inland and up to an altitude of ten thousand feet, and they lived for many months on the high, barren surface of the ice sheet. Their measurements in one place showed an ice thickness of six thousand two hundred feet. This figure does not mean that the Greenland Ice Sheet is everywhere more than a mile thick. Many such measurements are needed before we can hope to know the kind of land surface on which the glacier lies and can visualize what plains, plateaus, mountains and valleys are concealed beneath the thick and frigid blanket. We suspect that much of the terrain is mountainous, with rocky peaks sticking far up into the ice.

A close view of the Greenland Ice Sheet has occasionally been possible without a fatiguing climb requiring months of preparation. In one of the earlier war years, a Navy pontoon plane, with its crew of five, was making a routine patrol flight along the west coast of Greenland. Suddenly, as is all too common in coastal Greenland, the weather thickened, and within a few minutes the visibility shrank to zero. The pilot climbed to a safe altitude—some thousands of feet—and continued on his way. For a time nothing happened; then the plane seemed to slow down, and, glancing at his air-speed indicator, the pilot was amazed to see the needle swing gradually over to zero! Nothing but mist was visible, but it was evident that the plane had stopped. Climbing gingerly out, the crew discovered that their ship was resting comfortably on the snow-covered Greenland Ice Sheet, above the level of the mountain tops! Blindly and unsuspectingly, they had come in at just the right angle, along the contour of the sloping ice sheet, and the deep snow had comfortably cushioned their landing.

The plane was undamaged, but the crew were unable to turn it around into take-off position. Accordingly, they radioed for aid, and after two or three days of waiting in warm Arctic clothing, and with emergency rations and an electric grill, they were rescued by a ground party with dog sledges. Their only discomfort came during the sledge journey down over the ice to the shore!

The abandoned plane was left on the ice sheet. How soon, if ever, it will be covered with snow and thus gradually enclosed within the glacier is a matter that will be decided by the contest between snowfall, wind-drifting and melting. Stray airplanes stranded on the Greenland Ice Sheet are not necessarily snowed in. This is illustrated by the story of one of the early attempts at a transatlantic flight.

In the summer of 1928, B.R.H. ("Fish") Hassell made a bold attempt to fly from Rockford, Illinois, to Sweden via Labrador and Greenland. Thick weather prevented his finding a planned refueling point on the west coast of Greenland, and he flew around until he ran out of gas. Finally he landed well inland on the ice sheet. He and Cramer, his mechanic, made a cold and dismal forced march of ten days down the treacherous ice to the coast, arriving at tidewater just as a University of Michigan geological expedition was on the point of departing for the year—and thus, by one day, they were saved.

Most people supposed that the little airplane abandoned on the ice sheet would be covered up with snow and gradually enclosed within the glacier. But sixteen years later, in 1944, a party from an Army Air Force base discovered Hassell's plane just where it had been left. Its position was so exposed that instead of burying it, the snow had drifted away. One of the party rescued a fountain pen, a keepsake Hassell had left behind in his haste to abandon the plane, and returned to its grateful owner a pen older by a sixteen years' sojourn high on the ice sheet.

Since the development of the atomic bomb, people sometimes ask whether atomic bombs could be used to eliminate the great ice sheets of Greenland and the Antarctic Continent. Unhappily, the effect of one of these bombs, when dropped on a human community, is only too well established. But its destructiveness is limited to a radius of a few miles. How many bombs would it take to destroy even the superficial ice in the Antarctic Ice Sheet, with an area of five million square miles, to say nothing of disposing of the deeper parts of the ice sheet, two thousand feet or more below the present surface? The atom bomb is surely not the answer. Indeed, we know of no means of melting the great volumes of polar ice, except by patiently waiting for a warm climate to do its slow work.

Those who suggest that we do away with our big ice sheets cannot have stopped to consider what would happen to our coastal lands, including many of our largest cities, if such a thing could somehow be made to happen. The two million or more cubic miles of ice thus converted into water would pour into the sea, raising the level of the oceans throughout the world by an amount estimated at seventy to one hundred feet. How much inhabited land lies less than seventy feet above present sea level? For a start, large parts of Boston, New York, Philadelphia and New Orleans lie within this vulnerable zone, not to mention many others among the world's great cities. . . . Consider this, and you will probably decide that the polar ice had better be left undisturbed.

It is hardly surprising to find most of the world's glaciers in or near the polar regions. There is, however, one great difference between the two polar regions. The south polar region is a continent covered by a great ice sheet that reaches ten thousand feet above sea level. The north polar region, on the other hand, is largely sea, most of which is filled with frozen sea water in the form of floating ice. Therefore, although it is proper to speak of a South Polar or Antarctic Ice Cap, it is incorrect to speak of a North Polar or Arctic Ice Cap. The only large ice cap, or ice sheet, in or near the north polar region is the Greenland Ice Sheet.

Although the lion's share of the world's ice is situated in high latitudes, there are, nevertheless, glaciers in Africa, South America and even New Guinea—regions directly on, or almost on, the equator itself. True, the equatorial belt includes the low-lying basins of the Amazon and the Congo, but it also includes some high mountains. In Ecuador, the Andes, more than eighteen thousand feet above sea level, have glaciers. So do the three highest peaks in equatorial East Africa: Ruwenzori, Kenya and Kilimanjaro, sixteen thousand to nineteen thousand feet above sea level. And high on the sixteen-thousand foot mountains of central New Guinea, surrounded by hot, steaming tropical rain forest, are two small ice sheets! All these ice bodies exist because of the low temperatures at such high altitudes, and because of abundant snowfall brought by moist winds blowing from nearby oceans. The combination of low temperature and abundant moisture is the key to the existence of glaciers anywhere in the world.

Are these and other glaciers maintaining themselves in health and vigor, or are they gradually disappearing? The answer to this question is easy, because we have the records of many observations made in recent years and in the historical past. During the last hundred years or so, glaciers the world over have been on the decline, and they are still dwindling. Since the time of the exploration and settlement of western United States, some of the smaller ones in that region have disappeared completely. This is a serious matter for communities in the Pacific Northwest that get their power from electric installations on streams fed largely by glacial melting water. If the present trend should continue, these people can look forward to a time—and not far in the future, either—when their power supply will virtually disappear.

The question of whether this world-wide shrinking of glaciers will continue indefinitely is closely connected with the familiar question: Are the glaciers of today relics of the "Ice Age"? Until recently it was widely believed that our glaciers are vestiges of those cold prehistoric times. However, recent research has led us to believe that, although the big ice sheets are "Ice Age" survivors, thousands of the smaller glaciers of today are only a few thousand years old. These glaciers were "reborn" about the time of the earlier Egyptian civilizations, when chillier world climates followed upon a period when climates were, in general, warmer than they are today. This climatic change implies that the earth's temperature has not been growing uninterruptedly colder since the "Ice Age." If the temperature trend has reversed in the historical past, we see no reason why it cannot do so again; and so it is not at all certain that we are moving steadily toward a glacier-free world.

The Study of the Sea and Its Relation to Man
By Claude E. ZoBell

. . . Approximately 71 per cent, or more than one hundred and forty million square miles, of the earth's surface is covered with water. The mean depth of the sea is about twelve thousand, five hundred feet. This may be contrasted with the mean elevation of the land above sea level, two thousand, three hundred feet. The greatest elevation in the world above sea level, Mount Everest in the Himalayas, is twenty-nine thousand one hundred and forty-one feet, while the greatest known depression, the Challenger Deep off Guam, is thirty-five thousand, six hundred feet in depth. If all the irregularities of the earth's surface were smoothed out, the resulting sphere would be covered with about seven thousand, five hundred feet of water.

This great mass of sea water, three hundred and thirty million cubic miles, directly or indirectly, influences the life of every inhabitant of the earth, regardless of whether he lives in the Sahara Desert or the South Sea Islands. World weather, climate, precipitation and the carbon dioxide content of the atmosphere are all influenced by the ocean. The vertical and horizontal movements of large masses of water of different temperatures affect the humidity and temperature of the overlying atmosphere, thereby creating high- or low-pressure areas, world-wide air movements, precipitation and other weather elements. That warm or cold ocean currents affect the climate of the adjacent land is well known. Transportation and communications are influenced by the oceans of the world, and the sea contains a great wealth of biological and mineral resources. Exclusive of insects, of which there are some four hundred and fifty thousand described species, four-fifths of all other species of animals known to man live in the sea, including forty thousand species of mollusks (oysters, clams, shellfish, etc.), nearly as many crustacea (lobsters, crabs, barnacles, etc.), and fifteen thousand species of marine fish. The plant kingdom is represented by eight thousand marine species. Many of these plants and animals are of commercial importance.

Vast stores of mineral wealth are to be found in the oceans of the world. Sea water contains an average of 3.5 per cent of mineral matter. About 85 per cent of the total is sodium chloride or common table salt. Large quantities of salt are reclaimed from the sea, solar salterns at San Diego and San Francisco alone yielding more than two million barrels a year. The Pacific Ocean contains enough salt to cover the continental United States to a depth of nearly a mile. Incidentally, the salinity of the ocean is not perceptibly increasing in spite of the fact that the rivers of the world annually carry in five trillion tons of salt.

Nearly every known mineral element has been demonstrated in sea water, some in commercially procurable quantities. Magnesium, which is used in many alloys, is being extracted from sea water in large quantities. Also extracted from sea water are sodium and potassium. Like iodine, potassium—until recently—could not be extracted profitably except from certain seaweeds which concentrate these elements. Sea water itself contains only 0.037 per cent of potassium, while dried kelp contains from 10 to 14 per cent. Similarly, there is only 0.0000005 per cent of iodine in sea water, but certain seaweeds contain 0.2 to 0.5 per cent when dried. At current prices a cubic mile of sea water contains $60,000,000 worth of iodine.

Long before it was known that bromine would be useful in the preparation of lead tetraethyl, used in high-compression motor fuels, oceanographic research had demonstrated that sea water contains 0.0065 per cent of bromine. Today, bromine extracted from the sea is virtually indispensable to the operation of automobiles, planes and similar mechanized equipment. However, we need have no apprehensions of a shortage so long as we have access to the sea, because a cubic mile of sea water contains two hundred and fifty thousand tons of bromine, and methods for its extraction are steadily being improved. As needs develop and chemical and metallurgical processes are perfected, more and more use will be made of the mineral resources of the sea.

Tremendous quantities of chlorine used in the chemical industries, manufacturing and chemical warfare are being taken from the inexhaustible supply in the sea.

The much heralded gold content, amounting to more than thirty trillion dollars' worth in the oceans of the world, or enough of this precious metal to give every one of the two billion inhabitants of the earth $15,000 worth each, is only a paper asset, because it costs more to extract it than it is worth.

However, the greatest wealth of the sea is not to be found in its mineral resources, but in its natural productivity, in plants as well as animals. Almost two hundred thousand species of animals are known to live in the sea and eight thousand species of plants grow there in abundance. In addition to their academic interest, many of these aquatic organisms are of commercial significance. Methods of conserving the plant and animal resources and methods of increasing or improving the biological productivity of the sea are practical problems meriting attention. The solution of such problems requires information on the food habits, cultural requirements, life histories, migrations, rates of growth and a multiplicity of other factors which influence the organisms in the marine environment.

Accumulating evidence indicates that, acre for acre the world over, the sea is more productive than the land. The primary production (organic matter produced by photosynthetic organisms) of certain areas, such as the Gulf of California, for example, appears to compare favorably with that of fertile garden soil, and it is believed that there are far fewer barren acres in the sea than on the land. There is never any drought in the sea, even temperatures prevail, and sea water is a perfectly balanced salt solution with only nitrates, phosphates and possibly silicates sometimes becoming factors which limit plant growth. Moreover, whereas only the topmost few inches of the soil are productive, photosynthetic organisms grow throughout the water to a depth limited only by the penetration of sunlight, this being two hundred to eight hundred feet depending upon the latitude, season, water turbulence, atmospheric moisture, abundance of organisms in the water and other factors. Then it is found that Arctic and Antarctic waters are quite productive in contradistinction to the barrenness of the land at high latitudes. . . .

A few thickly populated countries, notably Japan, Belgium, Holland and the Scandinavian countries, are now profitably practicing aquiculture or the cultivation of shellfish and certain seaweeds. Aquiculture seems to hold almost unlimited possibilities for producing food and other products. Students of the subject aver that aquiculture is just as susceptible to scientific treatment as agriculture. This is a field in which scientists studying the sea have made, and can yet make, many important contributions. . . .

Exploration of the ocean floor is another department of oceanographic research which has many practical applications. The study of cores of sedimentary material, collected from the bottom of the sea in long tubes attached to the end of a dredging cable, yields information of geological and paleontological significance. Most sedimentary rocks were formed in ancient seas, and the process is still going on in all its stages. Cores of stratified material a few feet in length provide a geological record of the part of the earth from which they came. . . .

Contrary to popular conception, the topography of the ocean floor is more irregular than that of the better known world above sea level. Towering mountains rise precipitously from the floor of the ocean, forming submarine ridges, reefs, banks and islands. Between the mountains are abyssal basins, depressions, trenches, deeps and canyons. The Mindanao and Ramapo Deeps, which descend more than six miles below sea level, are just a few miles from land. Recent studies at the Scripps Institution of Oceanography have dealt with submarine canyons near La Jolla and Monterey where within a mile of the mainland the sea bottom drops off precipitously. The seaward extension of the Hudson River Valley is another example of a submarine canyon.

Except in the neighborhood of rivers, harbors, anchorages, bays, estuaries and in close proximity to the land in general, relatively little is known concerning the extent and nature of the topographical features of the sea bottom because so few soundings have been made. As late as 1928 there was an area of two million square miles, one-half the area of the United States, in the southern Pacific in which only eight soundings had been made! In fact, the sea bottom is still a great unexplored wilderness for the most part. There are thousands of miles of uncharted waters along coasts where information on the bottom topography would be of great value in connection with military landing operations and the navigation of submarines.

The contour of the ocean floor affects oceanic circulation as well as the distribution of marine organisms. Different animal associations are found at different depths, and in certain regions the animal population on one side of a submarine ridge may be quite different from that on the other side. Shoals and banks provide some of the best fishing grounds.

Since the stability of the earth's crust is intimately associated with sedimentation in the sea and the physiography of the sea floor, fuller knowledge of the latter might disclose the locations where many great earthquakes originate. Some students of the subject believe that the high waves which occasionally devastate our shores have their origin in the tremendous submarine rock slides—a subject for further research. Also, a detailed picture of the topographical features of the sea bottom would aid in the navigation of vessels, especially of submerged submarines equipped with appropriate echo depth finders.

Hundreds of miles of expensive transoceanic communications cable have been saved, and still greater savings are possible, by knowing from a detailed picture of the ocean floor exactly how much cable must be payed out to insure its resting on the sea bottom and not suspended precariously from one submarine ridge to another where it may eventually break owing to its own weight. Lack of knowledge of the contour and character of the sea floor resulted in the failure of the first attempts to span the Atlantic with a cable. Now, two dozen transatlantic cables connect North America and Europe. Detailed soundings of the Atlantic crossings during the decade ending in 1930 have effected a saving of 8 to 10 per cent in the length of cable laid as compared with earlier projects.

The early mariner determined the depth of water under his vessel by lowering a weighted hemp line to the bottom and then measuring the length of the line in terms of fathoms, a fathom (six feet) being the length of line held by the outstretched arms of a man of average size. Later, greater depths were sounded by lowering a lead weight on the end of a steel piano wire and noting the revolutions of a pulley of known circumference over which the wire passed. Finally, the echo-sounding depth finder was developed. With this device an oscillation or sound wave is directed from the vessel to the bottom of the sea, whence the oscillation is reflected or echoed upward again. The return oscillation is picked up by a microphone and amplified so that it can be detected in the pilot house. By knowing the rate at which the oscillation travels through water and the time required for it to go down and back again, the depth of the water can be calculated. Most modern vessels are equipped with echo depth finders which aid them in finding their positions and especially in avoiding dangerous shoals. Also, supersonic echo meters are used successfully by certain fishing fleets for detecting the presence of schools of fish because the short waves are reflected by the fish in a recognizable pattern. These devices are being perfected to locate submarines even when their engines are not running. However, precise results require information on many characteristics of the water masses involved.

Every year, physical oceanographers are making important contributions to our knowledge of the circulatory movement of the water. It is commonly recognized that the horizontal movements of large masses of water have a pronounced effect upon local climatic conditions. This is exemplified by effects of the Labrador Current on the east coast as contrasted with that of the California Stream on the west coast. The vertical circulation or upwelling of large masses of cold water in temperate or tropical regions is equally or even more important in its effect upon oceanic as well as terrestrial conditions. Water from depths exceeding one thousand feet is almost invariably cold (30° to 38° F.), and it also differs in fertility, salinity, oxygen content and in other respects from surface water.

It will be appreciated at once that oceanic circulation influences the distribution of temperature, oxygen, salinity and marine organisms. The temperature of the water influences the growth of plants and animals in the sea. The surface temperature of large masses of water also influences the evaporation of water and hence precipitation (rainfall) as well as atmospheric circulation (wind), not only over the sea, but over the land also. Thus world weather is influenced by the horizontal and vertical circulation of the sea. Many meteorologists believe that data on oceanic conditions may serve as a rational basis for forecasting, sometimes several weeks in advance, the general features of the weather for a given part of the world. However, the extension and improvement of these forecasts require more data on oceanic circulation and the distribution of water temperatures.

On the east coast of the United States it has been found that the transport volumes, velocity and width of the Gulf Stream fluctuate from year to year. Some years, this great stream of warm tropical water is a hundred miles closer to the coast than in other years, thereby materially altering climatic conditions in the New England states. Recent studies show that the velocity and width of the Gulf Stream can be forecast from data obtained in the Gulf of Mexico, and such forecasts are of inestimable value. In fact, there are some indications that the effects may be even more far-reaching, extending into the North Sea and the adjacent countries. . . .

Knowledge of the ocean currents expedites, cheapens and safeguards navigation. Ignorance of the direction and velocity of the currents frequently results in discrepancies between the true position of the ship as determined by astronomical sights and that calculated for her by dead reckoning. The savings of time and fuel which result from charting the course of a vessel so that she goes with the current rather than against it, especially for slow freighters, are self-evident. While most of the major surface currents have been charted for many years, there are many systems of oceanic circulation about which little or nothing is known.

Mechanical effects of water movements may be noted along the coast. In many places the combined action of waves and currents is permitting the sea to encroach upon the land from a fraction of an inch to several feet each year. In other places, harbors and channels are being silted up and beaches altered. An example of the desirability of understanding ocean currents before planning coastal improvements is the million-dollar Santa Barbara yacht harbor. Though but few years have passed since the completion of this project, the harbor is silting up so that it continually requires expensive dredging, and the bathing beach for a considerable distance has been eroded by the altered currents.

Numerous devices have been proposed, patented or tried for harnessing the seemingly limitless power of the waves and tides. . . . Such potential sources of power must not be overlooked, but it is yet to be shown that they can compete with power from other sources. . . .

In conclusion it should be emphasized that while oceanographic research has done much to solve the mysteries of the deep, our knowledge of the sea is still woefully scant.

For obvious reasons, scientists at the Scripps Institution of Oceanography, and others elsewhere, have with few exceptions concentrated their efforts upon a study of contiguous coastal waters and local problems. Consequently, in spite of the efforts of international committees charged with the responsibility of promoting the study of the sea on a world-wide basis, there are extensive unexplored areas and countless unsolved problems. It is becoming increasingly apparent that a complete understanding of oceanic phenomena and their effects on terrestrial conditions requires information about more distant deep-sea regions. Oceanographic research is international in scope and requires the unified efforts of chemists, physicists, meteorologists, mathematicians, geologists and biologists having specialized training. However, in spite of the complexities and magnitude of the problems which challenge the ingenuity of marine scientists, progress is being made. The practical aspects of oceanographic research, together with the natural curiosity of man, should insure the continuation and expansion of the investigations of this last great unexplored frontier.

The Make of the Desert

By John C. VanDyke

The Bottom of the Bowl

In the ancient days when the shore of the Pacific was young, when the white sierras had only recently been heaved upward and the desert itself was in a formative stage, the ocean reached much farther inland than at the present time. It pushed through many a pass and flooded many a depression in the sands, as its wave marks upon granite bases and its numerous beaches still bear witness. In those days that portion of the Colorado Desert known as the Salton Basin did not exist. The Gulf of California extended as far north as the San Bernardino Range and as far west as the

Pass of San Gorgonio. Its waters stood deep where now lies the roadbed of the Southern Pacific Railway, and all the country from Indio almost to the Colorado River was a blue sea. The bowl was full. No one knew if it had a bottom or imagined that it would ever be emptied of water and given over to the drifting sands.

No doubt the tenure of the sea in this Salton Basin was of long duration. The sand dunes still standing along the northern shore—fifty feet high and shining like hills of chalk—were not made in a month; nor was the long, shelving beach beneath them—still covered with sea shells and pebbles and looking as though washed by the waves only yesterday—formed in a day. Both dunes and beach are plainly visible winding across the desert for many miles. The southwestern shore, stretching under a spur of the Coast Range, shows the same formation in its beach line. The old bays and lagoons that led inland from the sea, the river beds that brought down the surface waters from the mountains, the inlets and natural harbors are all in place. Some of them are drifted half full of sand, but they have not lost their identity. And out in the sea bed still stand masses of cellular rock, honeycombed and water-worn (and now for many years wind worn), showing the places where once rose the reefs of the ancient sea.

These are the only records that tell of the sea's occupation. The Indians have no tradition about it. Yet when the sea was there the Indian tribes were there also. Along the bases of the San Bernardino and San Jacinto Ranges there are indications of cave dwelling, rock-built squares that doubtless were fortified camps, heaps of stone that might have been burial mounds. Everywhere along the ancient shores and beaches you pick up pieces of pottery, broken ollas, stone pestles and mortars, ax heads, obsidian arrowheads, flint spear points, agate beads. There is not the slightest doubt that the shores were inhabited. It was a warm nook, accessible to the mountains and the Pacific; in fact, just the place where tribes would naturally gather. Branches of the Yuma Indians, like the Cocopas, overran all this country when the padres first crossed the desert; and it was probably their forefathers who lived by the shores of this Upper Gulf. No doubt they were fishermen, traders and fighters, like their modern representatives of Tiburon

Island; and no doubt they fished and fought and were happy by the shores of the mountain-locked sea.

But there came a time when there was a disturbance of the existing conditions in the Upper Gulf. Century after century the Colorado River had been carrying down to the sea its burden of sedimental sand and silt. It had been entering the Gulf far down on the eastern side at an acute angle. Gradually its deposits had been building up, banking up; and gradually the river had been pushing them out and across the Gulf in a southwesterly direction. Finally there was formed a delta dam stretching from shore to shore. The tides no longer brought water up and around the bases of the big mountains. Communication with the sea was cut off and what was once the top of the Gulf changed into an inland lake. It now had no water supply from below, it lay under a burning sun, and day by day evaporation carried it away.

No one knows how many days, how many years, elapsed before the decrease of the water became noticeable. Doubtless the lake shrunk away slowly from the white face of the sand dunes and the red walls of the mountains. The river mouths that opened into the lake narrowed themselves to small stream beds. The shelving beaches where the waves had fallen lazily year after year, pushing themselves over the sand in beautiful water mirrors, shone bare and dry in the sunlight. The ragged reefs, over which the choppy sea had tumbled and tossed so long, lifted their black hulks out of the water and with their hosts of barnacles and sea life became a part of the land.

The waters of the great inland lake fell perhaps a hundred feet and then they made a pause. The exposed shores dried out. They baked hard in the sun, and were slowly ground down to sand and powdered silt by the action of the winds. The waters made a long pause. They were receiving reinforcements from some source. Possibly there was more rainfall in those days than now, and the streams entering the lake from the mountains were much larger. Again there may have been underground springs. There are flowing wells today in this old sea bed—wells that cast up water saltier than the sea itself. No one knows their fountainhead. Perhaps by underground channels the water creeps through from the Gulf, or comes from mountain reservoirs and turns saline by passing through beds of salt. These are the might-bes; but it is far more probable that the Colorado River at high water had made a breach of some kind in the dam of its own construction and had poured overflow water into the lake by way of a dry channel called the New River. The bed of this river runs northward from below the boundary line of Lower California; and in 1893, during a rise in the Colorado, the waters rushed in and flooded the whole of what is called the Salton Basin. When the Colorado receded, the basin soon dried out again.

It was undoubtedly some accident of this kind that called the halt in the original recession. During the interim the lake had time to form new shores where the waves pounded and washed on the gravel as before until miles upon miles of new beach—pebbled, shelled and sloping downward with great uniformity—came into existence. This secondary beach is intact today and looks precisely like the primary except that it is not quite so large. Across the basin, along the southern mountains, the second water tracery is almost as apparent as the first. The rocks are eaten in long lines by wave action, and are honeycombed by the ceaseless energies of the zoöphite.

Nor was the change in beach and rock alone. New bays and harbors were cut out from where the sea had been, new river channels were opened down to the shrunken lake, new lagoons were spread over the flat places. Nature evidently made a great effort to repair the damage and adapt the lake to its new conditions. And the Indians, too, accepted the change. There are many indications in broken pottery, arrowheads and mortars that the aboriginal tribes moved down to the new beach and built wickiups by the diminished waters. And the old fishing-foraging-fighting life was probably resumed.

Then once more the waters went down, down, down. Step by step they receded until the secondary beach was left a hundred feet above the water level. Again there was a pause. Again new beaches were beaten into shape by the waves, new bays were opened, new arroyos cut through from above. The whole process of shore making—the fitting of the land to the shrunken proportions of the lake—was gone through with for the third time; while the water supply from the river or elsewhere was maintained in decreased volume but with some steadiness of flow. Possibly the third halt of the receding water was not for a great length of time. The tertiary beach is not so large as its predecessors. There never was any strong wave action upon it, its pebbles are few, its faults and breaks are many. The water supply was failing, and finally it ceased altogether.

What fate for a lake in the desert receiving no supplies from river or sea—what fate save annihilation? The hot breath of the wind blew across the cramped water and whipped its surface into little waves; and as each tiny point of spray rose on the crest and was lifted into the air the fiery sunbeam caught it, and in a twinkling had evaporated and carried it upward. Day by day this process went on over the whole surface until there was no more sea. The hollow reefs rose high and dark above the bed, the flat shoals of silt lifted out of the ooze, and down in the lowest pools there was the rush and plunge of monster tortuabas, sharks and porpoises, caught as it were in a net and vainly struggling to get out. How strange must have seemed that landscape when the low ridges were shining with the slime of the sea, when the beds were strewn with algae, sponges and coral, and the shores were whitening with salt! How strange, indeed, must have been the first sight of the bottom of the bowl!

But the sun never relaxed its fierce heat nor the wind its hot breath. They scorched and burned the silt of the sea bed until it baked and cracked into blocks. Then began the wear of the winds upon the broken edges until the blocks were reduced to dry, fine powder. Finally the desert came in. Drifts upon drifts of sand blown through the valleys settled in the empty basin, gravel and boulder wash came down from the mountains; the greasewood, the salt bush, and the so-called peppergrass sprang up in isolated spots. Slowly the desert fastened itself upon the basin. Its heat became too intense to allow the falling rain to reach the earth, its surface was too salt and alkaline to allow of much vegetation, it could support neither animal nor bird life; it became more deserted than the desert itself.

And thus it remains to this day. When you are in the bottom of it you are nearly three hundred feet below the level of the sea. Circling about you to the north, south and west are sierras, some of them over ten thousand feet in height. These form the rim of the bowl. And off to the southward there is a side broken out of the bowl through which you can pass to the river and the Gulf. The basin is perhaps the hottest place to be found anywhere on the American deserts. And it is also the most forsaken. The bottom itself is, for the greater part of it, as flat as a table. It looks like a great plain leading up and out to the horizon —a plain that has been plowed and rolled smooth. The soil is drifted silt—the deposits made by the washings from the mountains—and is almost as fine as flour.

The long lines of dunes at the north are just as desolate, yet they are wonderfully beautiful. The desert sand is finer than snow, and its curves and arches, as it builds its succession of drifts out and over an arroyo, are as graceful as the lines of running water. The dunes are always rhythmical and flowing in their forms; and for the color the desert has nothing that surpasses them. In the early morning, before the sun is up, they are air-blue, reflecting the sky overhead; at noon they are pale lines of dazzling orange-colored light, waving and undulating in the heated air; at sunset they are often flooded with a rose or mauve color; under a blue moonlight they shine white as icebergs in the northern seas. . . .

PART THREE

Structure and Composition of the Earth

IN THE FIRST SECTION of this book Arthur Holmes described briefly the surface relief of the earth and the nature of its crust. In the first article in the present section on "X-Raying the Earth," Reginald A. Daly, noted Professor of Geology at Harvard, takes us down into the earth and shows us how the geophysicist, by means of waves, has penetrated the earth's crust, then delved into its interior in an attempt to interpret its nature. In this way, as he tells us, the shelled character of our planet was discovered, and the inner core was found. Yet if a great deal has been found out, many questions have also been raised which still await definite answer.

What is the composition of the inner core? What is its physical state? Are the shells uniform and more or less static? Or are they, as some geologists now think, unevenly formed as a result of the tremendous dynamic activity which seems to be going on in the far from "solid earth" under our feet? If the earth's core is mobile, as now seems likely, is this fact important in solving the difficult problem of the slow rising and sinking of great areas of the earth's crust? In the core very high temperatures and great pressures exist. Do these factors also have anything to do with the extraordinary process of mountain building? Samuel J. Shand discusses baffling questions like these in the second article of this section, "The Problem of Mountains."

Dr. Shand takes us from the Alps to the Himalayas, from the Sierras to the Jordan Sea, in order to describe the different types of mountains which, at different periods in the earth's history, have been formed in different ways. He discusses some of the theories which have been offered to explain folding and faulting, rifts and ramps. Thus he describes the contraction theory, in which the shrinking and possibly the cooling of the earth core have been used to explain the strange wrinkling of the earth's face.

Dr. Shand also refers briefly to the problem of volcanoes, where the processes are more clearly understood. These extraordinary phenomena have roused fear among the ancients and awe even among modern scientists. They seem to occur mostly in young mountain belts, where the earth's face has recently been wrinkled and cracked, and to come from the very hot shell which lies deep down in the earth's interior. This shell is composed of crystalline material which, when the pressure on it is reduced or the temperature rises, becomes liquefied. The magma, lighter than the rocks surrounding it, pushes its way up toward the earth's surface, and if it finds a fracture in that surface, emerges in a flood of fluid lava. If, on the other hand, as often happens, it hits a layer of solid rock, it will flow sideways, forming a reservoir until it finds a crack in the rock layer. It will then push its way through the rock and erupt as a violent volcano.

One of the most spectacular volcanic eruptions in this century in this hemisphere occurred in Mexico in 1942. The dramatic story of that eruption is told in "The Birth of Parícutin" by Jenaro Gonzalez, a Mexican geologist, and William F. Foshag, Head Curator of the Department of Geology in the United States National Museum. For some time before the eruption gases had been escaping from a small vent in the earth. Then one day the surrounding country began to tremble. For twenty days the trembling continued and the shocks increased in number as well as strength. Then, suddenly, to the amazement of the farmer who owned it, the volcano was born in the middle of his field.

In the case of Parícutin, we are dealing with active lava, hot and fluid. Yet all over the earth, as Carey Croneis and William C. Krumbein show in "Rocks and Minerals," there are "frozen seas of lava"—in scientific language, igneous rocks, which were formed by the hardening of lava flows and give evidence of even greater volcanic activity in ancient times. Again, rocks which once were liquid in the magma under the earth's surface hardened there and never reached the surface. These igneous rocks, as Holmes showed in his classification, form one of three great classes into which the rocks of the earth are divided —igneous, metamorphic and sedimentary.

Croneis and Krumbein first tell us how igneous rocks originate, then how they are studied by methods which require knowledge of chemistry as well as of physics. As we shall see, the rocks are composed of minerals, and the minerals in turn are made of atoms of chemical elements. We now know that, of all the elements known, nine are so abundant that they make up more than 99 per cent of all the thousands of rocks that have been analyzed. Oxygen is by far the most abundant, while silicon comes next. As Croneis and Krumbein show, these two elements have a great deal to do with the formation of one of the most common and familiar of minerals—quartz.

From igneous rocks they turn to the next great class— the metamorphic. These rocks were originally igneous or sedimentary, but are so radically changed by their environment that they no longer resemble the original. Heat and pressure, time and chemical change—all these act to change structure and mineral composition. This, in contrast to the process of weathering and erosion described in the second section of this book, is a constructive rather than a destructive process. Often the original rock, dull and uninteresting, assumes a much more beautiful crystalline form.

In the last article in this section C. C. Furnas, formerly Associate Professor of Chemical Engineering at Yale, now Director of the Cornell Aeronautical Laboratory in Buffalo, considers the vital part played by living organisms in the building up of the earth's surface and in the "Formation of Mineral Deposits." He discusses also the still puzzling problem of the origin of petroleum, which must finally be solved by joint work of the chemist, the geologist, even of the biologist, working in the field and in the laboratory.

X-Raying the Earth

By Reginald A. Daly

Reality is never skin deep. The true nature of the earth and its full wealth of hidden treasures cannot be argued from the visible rocks, the rocks upon which we live and out of which we make our living. The face of the earth, with its upstanding continents and depressed ocean deeps, its vast ornament of plateau and mountain chain, is molded by structure and process in hidden depths.

During the nineteenth century the geologists, a mere handful among the world's workers, studied the rocks at the surface, the accessible skin of the globe. They established many principal points in our planet's history. While with the astronomers space was deepening, a million years became for the rock men the unit of time with which to outline the earth's dramatic story. Thus, incidentally, the way was opened for the doctrine of organic evolution, demanding hundreds of millions of years, to become secured science rather than mere speculation. The first main jobs of the geologist were to map the exposures of the rocks at the surface of the earth skin or "crust," to distinguish the kinds and relative ages of the rocks, to gather the many facts that must be accounted for in the final explanation of continent, ocean, plateau and mountain range. Yet the century closed without having disclosed clearly defined origins for these and of many another form and structure of the earth's surface and "crust." With increasing clearness geologists became convinced, however, that the main secret of highland and lowland, dry land and deep ocean, Himalaya and Mediterranean, barren rock and ore-bearing rock, must be sought in the invisible, the deep underground of the earth.

The nineteenth century bequeathed to the twentieth an outstanding responsibility—to invent and use new methods of exploring the earth's body far beyond the reach of direct penetration by the geologist's eye or by mine and bore hole. What is the nature of the materials below the visible rocks? How are those materials arranged? What energies are stored in the globe, ready to do geological work when the occasion comes? Where is the earth's body strong, truly solid, able to bear loads indefinitely? Where is it weak, so weak as to permit movements of the material horizontally and vertically under the urge of moderate internal pressures?

These questions represent fundamentals of the new earth lore, already rapidly growing in our own century as investigators continue to employ new methods of research. The problems are largely matters for the physicist, but an unusual kind of physicist, one who makes experiments, like any of his fellows, but keeps thinking of a whole planet. He is an earth physicist, a "geophysicist." The interpretation of messages from the earth's interior demands all the resources of ordinary physics and of extraordinary mathematics. The geophysicist is of a noble company, all of whom are reading messages from the untouchable reality of things. The inwardness of things—atoms, crystals, mountains, planets, stars, nebulas, universes—is the quarry of these hunters of genius and Promethean boldness. The unseen atom has been shown to be no less miraculous than the invisible interior of sun or star. And now, lately, the inner earth as a whole is the gripping subject of research for some of the intellectual giants of our time. To a considerable extent the methods used by all these students of the invisible, the essence of each problem, are in principle the same.

The feature common to most of the productive methods is the use of waves, vibrations, rhythmic motions. From the interior of star or nebula come light waves, heat waves and whole troops of different unfelt waves. Each of these waves, whatever its nature, radiates through the "ether." With the speed of light, each rushes along lines that are always perpendicular to the front of the wave. These lines are the wave paths or "rays" of the astrophysicist. In the exploration of the universe of stars, he uses light rays, actinic rays, heat rays, and cosmic rays of less familiar kinds. The exquisite internal architecture of crystals is being rapidly revealed with X-rays. The atom is becoming understood through its radiant effects and through experimental tests with external rays.

So it is with the new study of the earth; its profounder exploration is possible by means of waves, which may be of either natural or artificial origin. Waves extremely short, as measured from "crest" to "crest," are the X-rays, used in learning the atomic architecture of crystals. The somewhat longer waves of light tell us about the nature of stars. The still longer sound waves are now used to give the depths of the invisible ocean floor. "Radio" waves, yet longer, are telling the aerologists much about the nature of the inaccessible upper atmosphere. For the study of the earth's skin, to the depths of a score of miles or so, the controlled shocks by artificial explosives, which give elastic waves longer than even "radio" waves, are used. Longest of all are the elastic waves set going when the hammer of the deadly earthquake strikes. Man is learning to harness for his inquiring use the very wrath of the earth; the tremblings of our vibrant globe are used to "X-ray" the deep interior.

When with his hands one bends a stick until it breaks, the sudden snap sends vibrations, often painful, along muscle, bone and nerve of the arms. The "strain" of the stick is relieved by fracture, and the elastic energy accumulated in the stick during the bending is largely converted into the energy of wave motion. In a somewhat similar way the rocks of the earth's crust have been, and now are being, strained; every day, somewhere, they are snapping and sending out elastic waves from one or more centers. The passage of these waves in the earth we call an earthquake, a seismic disturbance.

Each heavy shock creates waves of several kinds. The kind which travels fastest is like a sound wave; it is propagated by the alternation of compression and rarefaction in the rocks. The particles of the rocks here vibrate to and fro, in the direction of wave motion, that is, along the wave path or wave "ray." Waves of this type, technically called longitudinal waves, can pass from rock into the fluid of ocean, lake or atmosphere, and if the vibrations are frequent enough, are heard with the unaided ear. Somewhat slower is a second kind of wave which follows nearly the same path in the rocks, but is distinguished by the fact that now the rock particles vibrate at right angles to the direction of propagation. Waves of the second type, called transverse seismic waves, are propagated in solids only and cannot pass through a liquid or gas.

These two kinds of waves, longitudinal and transverse, each radiating from the center of shock, correspond after a fashion to the X-rays used by the surgeon for exploring the deep inside of the human body. Similarly, the deep inside of the earth is being explored with the two kinds of seismic (earthquake) waves, waves whose diverging paths, or "rays," plunge right down into the vast interior of the globe and emerge, with their messages, thousands of miles from the center of shock. The longitudinal waves emerge even at the antipodes.

A major earthquake has enormous energy. At and near the center of shock it shatters the works of man and may rupture the very hills and mountain sides. As each wave front spreads into the earth, the intensity of the vibration falls very rapidly, so that a few hundreds of miles from the center the heaviest shock cannot be felt by a human being. Much less can he, at the "other side" of the globe, feel the impact of a wave which has plunged to a depth of a thousand miles or more and emerges under his feet.

In order to watch and time accurately each wave, as its ray emerges on the "other side," highly sensitive instruments are used. These wonderful instruments, called seismographs, magnify the motion of the vibrating rock and give a written record, or "graph," of that motion. They form the main equipment of seismographic stations. The mechanical or photographic record of a distant shock is the seismogram, a kind of hieroglyphic message from the mysterious heart of the planet. Each seismogram from a strong earthquake is a long, complex curve traced up and down on the registering paper of the seismograph. Usually the impulses of the longitudinal and transverse waves are evident to the expert seismologist, but in every case he finds represented much more than these two simple kinds of motion. He sees, in fact, a whole train of waves, which came racing out of the earth, often for much more than an hour after the first impulse was registered. A generation ago, most of the complex message could not be read. Then seismologists bethought themselves of a Rosetta stone.

Observation and theory soon showed that earthquake

waves are closely analogous to the familiar waves of sound and light. Like these, the seismic rays are reflected and refracted at surfaces between different kinds of material. Seismic rays, during their passage through the earth, are broken up and dispersed, just as the sun's light is dispersed, in prism or raindrop, to make the glory of the rainbow. Seismic rays are diffracted, just as light rays are diffracted, at the interfaces of contrasted materials. As sound travels faster in water than in air, faster in rock than in either, so seismic waves travel faster in some kinds of rock than in other kinds. Long study of sound and light has led to the discovery of the laws of wave motion, and these have made increasingly clear the meaning of seismograms. The analogy with sound and light is the Rosetta stone.

The discovery of the famous original enabled Napoleon's experts to begin the reading of Egypt's ancient literature. In like manner the seismologists, using the difficult but manageable Greek of modern physics, are beginning the task of making earthquakes tell the nature of the earth's interior and translating into significant speech the hieroglyphics written by the seismograph. It is a long task, requiring high intelligence and the patient accumulation of earthquake data from all parts of the globe, from ocean basin as well as from continent. The work is only just begun; yet the results already obtained are of supreme interest to the philosopher, to the geologist, and to the producer of petroleum, metals and other materials from the rocks.

For here, too, the man of pure science, the seismologist, "fussing with experiments of no use to anyone," has proved to be another goose that has laid a golden egg. The methods developed by the worker in another "pure" science, seismology, are now, with the help of artificial earthquakes, locating structures that lead to hidden deposits of oil. So, millions are to be saved in the cost of bore holes, and new oil, probably by the hundreds of millions of barrels, will be added to the world supply. With electrical, magnetic and gravitational methods—all products of the "unpractical" man of "pure" science—valuable indications of hidden metal-bearing ores are secured, and the expense of exploration by bore holes and shafts is greatly reduced. Seismological methods promise to be adaptable to this kind of detective work. Conquering the difficulties that still remain, future research should make this branch of geophysics, even in the search after metals, pay for its upkeep many times over.

The depths of the ocean are now being quickly and accurately measured by the echo of sound waves from the bottom of the sea. This method, incomparably more rapid and less expensive than the old one by sounding line, is based on a principle fundamental in seismology. With variation of detail, "sonic" sounding, the use of waves reflected from underlying rock, is employed to measure the thickness of glaciers.

Thus, the Hintereisferner Glacier of the Alps has been proved to be eight hundred and thirty feet thick in the middle. When, with the similar use of explosion shocks and the seismograph, the thickness of the entire Antarctic and Greenland Ice Caps are measured, we shall have precious data for guiding thought on the conditions of North America and Europe during the Glacial Period. Furthermore, we could then estimate how far the sea level was everywhere lowered when the water of these ice caps was abstracted from the ocean and piled up, solid, on the land.

But from depths far greater than glacier floor, ocean floor, or mineral deposit come the messages from nature's earthquakes. A few illustrations of success in detecting the anatomy of a planet will show the real majesty of the questions and answers that already inspire the all too few workers in the new science of geophysics.

One of the outstanding seismological discoveries of recent years is the shelled character of our planet. At the center, and outward to a little more than one-half of its radius, the earth is homogeneous in high degree. This so-called "core" is surrounded by successive shells or layers of material. Each shell, out to a level about thirty miles from the surface, is relatively homogeneous, and its material differs from that of the shell above or below, as well as from the material of the central core. The contacts between the shells and between the deepest shell and the core are technically called "discontinuities."

The discontinuity, or break of material, at the surface of the core is one of the most remarkable of all. It is located at a level about eighteen hundred miles below the earth's surface, nearly twenty-two hundred miles from its center.

A second principal break, found only under the continents and larger islands—and thus representing only parts of a complete earth shell—is situated at the average depth of about twenty-five miles. Other discontinuities, limiting complete shells of the earth's body, have been reported at depths of about seventy-five miles, two hundred and fifty miles, seven hundred and fifty miles, and eleven hundred miles. All of these four breaks require further study. Their estimated depths may be somewhat changed, and other discontinuities may be discovered, but it is already clear in a general way how the earth is constituted—layer on layer. There is good evidence that the core and layers described are composed of matter which increases in density as the depth increases. Hence, so far as the great body of the earth is concerned, it is built stable.

The velocity of the longitudinal wave in the earth's core has been measured. The value obtained is appropriate to that of the metallic iron of the meteorites. However, the velocity is lower than that expected if the core iron were crystalline and solid, like the iron of our museum meteorites. The velocity of the longitudinal wave suggests, rather, that the core iron is fluid. In agreement with this conclusion the slower, transverse wave seems not to be propagated through the core; we have learned that the transverse wave cannot persist in a fluid. If further research corroborates this tentative deduction by seismologists, a whole set of new, fascinating problems is opened up.

One question is that of temperature. The pressure on the core iron ranges from fifteen million to fifty million pounds to the square inch. Under such colossal pressure the iron can be fluid only on the condition that the temperature of the core is enormously high—at tens of thousands of degrees Centigrade. Both pressure and temperature are far beyond the range of the experimental laboratory. The physical state of the core iron cannot as yet be described. Is it a liquid, a gas or iron in a "state" unknown to physics? The conditions of the earth's core are starlike. From their study can physicists of the future tell us something more of the true nature of the stars? If they can, they will be pretty sure, incidentally, to shed new light on the structure and life story of the atoms; for the secret of the star and the secret of the atom are proving to be part of a single problem, the ultimate nature of matter.

Again, if the core is fluid, it is infinitely weak. It can offer no permanent resistance to forces which tend to distort the earth's body. Hence other questions for future research: Is this mobility of the earth's core important in the explanation of the slow upheavings and down-sinkings of great areas of the earth's "crust"? Is the sensitive core involved even in the tumult of mountain building? No one can now tell, but speculate we must, for it is today's speculation which leads to tomorrow's science.

The exact nature of the earth shells overlying the core and totaling fifteen hundred miles in thickness is another problem for the future. Presumably, the deepest of these shells is a more rigid, because cooler, chemical equivalent of the "fluid" core, but it is not yet clear how thick this more rigid "iron" may be. The published conclusions as to the composition and precise thicknesses of the still higher shells are uncertain and demand further testing. Yet the principle that the earth is layered seems proved once for all and leads to an apparently inescapable and highly significant conclusion. The shell structure of the earth seems to defy explanation unless it be assumed that our planet was formerly molten. It must have been fluid enough to stratify itself by gravity. The "heavier" materials sank toward the center, the "lighter" materials rose toward the surface, and the whole mass finally arranged itself as layers or shells, with the very dense iron in the central region. It seems necessary to assume primitive fluidity right to the surface, and, further, to assume that the earth was thus fluid after practically all of its substance had been collected in the planet-making process. This general deduction must control future research on the cosmogonic problem—the origin of the earth and its brothers and sisters of the solar system. The earth was born in fervent heat and in the beginning was fervently hot even at the surface.

While telling us much about the heart of the earth, the seismogram is still more authoritative and eloquent concerning the uppermost layers of the globe. By studying the instrumental records of the reflections, refractions, accelerations and retardations of earthquake waves, seismologists have found that the continental rocks reach downward about thirty miles. At that level there is a rather abrupt change to a world-circling shell of a quite different nature. The dominant rock of the continents is granite. According to the facts of geology, as of seismology, the underlying shell or substratum is the heavier, dark-colored basalt, and is apparently the source of this commonest of lavas and the primary seat of all volcanic energies.

The depth of the continental rock, so determined from the writing of the longitudinal and transverse waves on seismographs, is confirmed by study of a different kind of vibrations which come pouring into the station still later than the transverse wave. This third division of a typical seismogram is written by a long train of oscillations, corresponding to what are called surface waves, because they faithfully follow the great curve of the earth's rocky skin. Surface waves are the strongest of all the vibrations recorded by distant earthquakes. They are caused by the reflection of the longitudinal and transverse waves as these, coming from the interior, impinge at low angles upon the contact of rock with ocean water and of rock with the air. That contact acts like the walls of a gigantic whispering gallery. From the character and velocities of the surface waves, expert seismologists have corroborated the evidence, won from the longitudinal and transverse waves, concerning the nature and depth of the continental rock.

But the surface waves inform us also about the kind of rock immediately beneath the deep oceans, whose waters hide from view about two-thirds of the solid surface of the whole earth. The measured velocities of the surface waves show that the earth's skin beneath the deep oceans is crystallized basalt. Thus the material forming an earth shell directly beneath the continents is continuous with, and chemically identical with, the surface rock under the deep sea.

Granite, the principal rock of the continents, is a relatively light rock. Basalt, the essential rock beneath the oceans, is relatively heavy. It is for this reason that the continents float high on the earth's body; they are pressed up by the surrounding heavy, solid basalt, much as icebergs are pressed up by the denser water of the sea. This is why we have dry land, with its endless importance for man and organic life in general.

Seismology tells us why our hope is stable, in spite of mighty forces which tend to level the earth's crust and drown us all. We may confidently expect also that this continued "X-raying" of the outer earth will furnish new information as to the reason why mountains stand so high and are able to keep their heads in the clouds, far above the general level of the continents. And to geophysics, especially to seismology, we look for new help in finding out the conditions for the earth's periodic revolutions when mountain chains were born and sea bottoms became the pinnacles of the world.

The Problem of Mountains
By Samuel J. Shand

. . . The most surprising thing about the great mountain ranges of the world is that they are largely formed of sedimentary rocks, which we can recognize, by the fossils they contain, as having been laid down on the sea floor. . . . It is possible that the rate of movement may have been a little faster, at times, than any that we can observe at the present day, but there is no reason to think that it was much faster. . . . Part of the floor of the Baltic Sea is rising at such a rate that in a million years it might be as high as Mount Everest. It is quite certain, however, that Mount Everest was not raised as quickly as that. The Himalaya first began to rise above the sea at the close of the Cretaceous Period, which, if we can accept the estimates of geological time, may have been sixty million years ago; they continued to grow until at least the end of the Tertiary Period, and for aught we know they may be growing still. There is no evidence of jerry-building there.

Yet the movements that give rise to mountain ranges are not simple uplifts. They are primarily horizontal movements, and they have the effect of throwing the crust into wrinkles just like the wrinkles we make in a tablecloth when we push it about on the table. The Jura Mountains of

Switzerland are a series of nearly parallel wrinkles, or ridges and valleys, of this very simple type, and so—in parts—are the Appalachian Mountains of North America, which stretch from Alabama to Newfoundland. Other ranges are more complicated. The Alps in particular, which have been studied in greater detail than any other mountain range, show such astonishing complications that one despairs of explaining them except in barest outline. But even the Alps began with simple folds. If we raise a wrinkle on a tablecloth, it will generally be symmetrical at first, with

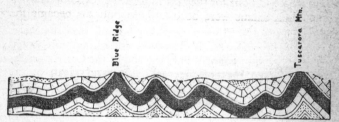

Simple folds in the Appalachian Mountains

similar slopes on both sides; but if we compress it more and more it will often become steeper on one side than on the other and then turn over until it overlaps the flat part of the tablecloth. It is now an overfold. Now, beds of rock are flexible to a certain extent, but far less so than any tablecloth; they can be thrown into folds and overfolds, as we can see in almost any mountain range, but there is a limit beyond which they will not bend any more but will break. When an overfold among beds of rock is compressed beyond that limit, it breaks, and the fracture generally takes place in the middle limb of the fold. Further compression leads to the upper flank of the fold being pushed bodily over the lower flank, along a gently inclined or nearly horizontal plane of fracture which geologists call a thrust plane. By further compression a second fold may be pushed over the first, a third over the second, and so on; or else the second fold may develop in front of the first, and as it advances it may carry the first along on its back. It is by the application of such ideas as these that the structure of a complex mountain range like the Alps can be made intelligible.

We shall try to summarize the history of the Alps as it has been brought to light by the joint labors of several generations of Swiss, French and Austrian geologists.

The oldest rocks of the Alps, which we can see in the Mont Blanc and Jungfrau areas, are granites and ancient sedimentary rocks that have been greatly altered by heat and pressure. The technical name for such rocks is crystalline schist. These rocks are relics of what was probably a mountain range in the Proterozoic Age. Round about these relics, after the Cambrian Period, there was a wide sea that covered most of Europe. In the deeper parts of this sea corals flourished and built up thick reefs of limestone; in the shallower parts the bottom deposits were, as usual, of a more sandy character. These conditions lasted with only minor changes until the end of the Carboniferous Period, when part of the sea basin lying north of the present Alps was raised above sea level and thrown into a series of folds, of which we can still trace the roots from the south of England across France and Germany and on into the Balkans. The sea was narrowed by this movement, but as time passed and the new land was exposed to erosion the sea spread again over much of its former territory, and sediment derived from the new land was spread over the sea floor, adding greatly to the thickness of what was already there. This pre-Alpine sea covered all that is now Central Europe and North Africa, and extended far across Asia. It was probably broken up by longitudinal ridges and islands, and was divided by these into basins within which different types of sediment were laid down. The most northerly basin is known as the Helvetian Basin, and south and southeast of it lay the Pennine Basin, the East Alpine Basin, and the Dinaric Basin or Sea, covering North Italy and the Balkans. The Helvetian Basin was a comparatively shallow one in which many beds of limestone were formed. The Pennine Basin was deeper and the deposits are of fine-grained, deep-sea character; and lava flows appear among them. The East Alpine Basin was deep at first, and acquired a great thickness of limestone and fine salty deposits, but the later sediments had a shallow-water character. The Dinaric region was deep, and in it thick beds of coral-limestone and dolomite were formed.

About the Cretaceous Period, earth movement was renewed; and the great thickness of sediments in the East Alpine Basin was compressed and thrown into folds. These folds afterward became overfolds, and eventually the East Alpine sediments were pushed northward over the sediments of the Pennine Basin, which sank beneath their weight. As fast as the folds rose above the sea they were exposed to erosion, and their detritus was deposited in front of them; and as the northward movement went on the sliding sheets of rock were sometimes thrust over their own detritus, so that older rocks came to lie on top of younger ones and deep-sea limestones on top of shallow-water pebble beds. In the west, at a later stage, the Pennine sediments were thrust over the Helvetian ores, carrying the East Alpine sheets on their back. In the end the northern part of the Dinaric Sea was also affected and the limestones and dolomites there were thrust over one another toward the south; thus the north and south flanks of the Alpine chain have been driven out in opposite directions. By the end of the Tertiary Period most of the horizontal movement was finished, and in the Quaternary Period the Alps grew chiefly in height. At the same time the mountains were exposed to intense erosion by water and ice, until from the heap of overthrust sheets of sediment there were carved out the Alps as we know them now. So great have the effects of erosion been, since the mountains rose above sea level, that parts of the upper overthrust sheets have been completely severed from their roots; thus the Pre-Alps of Chablais are regarded as relics of the East Alpine sheets and their roots lie on the south side of the main axis of the Alps.

Exact surveying shows that the Alpine movements are not yet quite finished and that the front of the Alps is still advancing over the northern plains, which are sinking in front of the mountains.

Told in these bald words, with most of the complications avoided and the doubts and difficulties ignored, the story is so strange as to be almost unbelievable. Instead of simple wrinkles like the Jura Mountains, the Alps prove to be formed of a series of sheets or wedges of rock that have been pushed up at low angles from the sea floor and thrust over one another, generally from south to north, but sometimes from north to south. The mechanism is at present beyond our comprehension, but the evidence is there; and the broad outline of the story has been accepted by every geologist who has studied the Alps. Naturally there is still a lack of agreement about many of the details; it is unlikely that full agreement will ever be reached about some aspects of this most complicated problem; but in what history are there no doubtful incidents? It is not as if the Alpine chain were unique in its mode of formation; entirely similar structures have been made out in Norway and the Highlands of Scotland, in the Rocky Mountains, and especially in the Himalaya. Overthrusting of sheet upon sheet of rock is characteristic of all these ranges; and even among simple-looking wrinkle mountains like the Jura and the Appalachians some degree of overthrusting can often be detected.

It is clear that as a result of wrinkling of the crust, and still more in consequence of overthrusting, some segments of the earth crust must have been appreciably narrowed in geological time. The belt of country where the Jura Mountains now stand is some three miles narrower than it was before the beds were thrown into wrinkles. If the Alps could be taken to bits, the folds flattened out and the over-thrust sheets pushed back where they came from, they would occupy a belt of country probably twice as wide as the present Alps. A recent study of the Appalachian Mountains shows that the present width of two hundred and seventy miles represents an original width of about five hundred miles. As for the Himalaya, although the geo-logical evidence is far from complete in that most difficult area, it is claimed that the distance between Siberia and India is shorter by perhaps four hundred miles than it was before the mountains arose from the sea.

The history of the Alps teaches us that the building of a mountain range demands a long period of preparation. Most strangely, the first stage in the preparation seems to be the formation of a submarine trough in which sediment accumulates to an altogether unusual thickness. The most puzzling aspect of the matter is that the trough does not always seem to be formed in advance of the filling, but to deepen gradually as sediment accumulates in it. . . .

The history of the Alps teaches us, too, that mountain-building movements are not continuous, but proceed by spasms; and when one compares mountain ranges in different parts of the world it seems that periods of active mountain building have been roughly contemporaneous in widely separated places. While the Alps were beginning to take shape in Europe, the Rocky Mountains were rising in North America, the Himalaya and other great chains in Asia and the Atlas in North Africa. The Carboniferous folding in Europe was contemporaneous with the building of the Appalachians in North America and the Cape ranges in South Africa. There was a still earlier period of

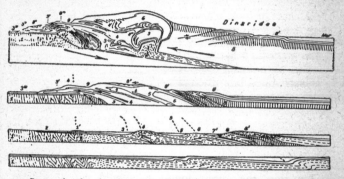

Stages in the development of the Alps (E. Argand, 1916)

mountain building in Europe, about the close of the Silurian Period, when great ranges were formed in Scotland and Norway of which the present mountains are only the deeply eroded stumps. The Cambrian Period, in most parts of the world, was preceded by great disturbances of the earth crust.

Such observations as these lend support to the view that mountain building is due to some deep-seated cause that affects the whole earth at once. It seemed to the early geologists that the explanation lay in the shrinkage of the earth core as it cools down. This would make the crust too big for the core, and it would be compelled to accommodate itself to the changing conditions by forming wrinkles. In spite of the simplicity and attractiveness of this explanation, it raises serious difficulties. Why, for instance, are the wrinkles confined to a few well-defined belts instead of being spread more or less uniformly over the whole surface of the globe? There are great regions such as Russia and eastern Canada where no mountain-building movements have taken place since the Proterozoic Period, and there is little indication of mountain ranges

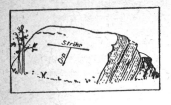 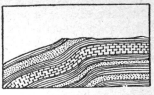

 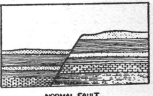

Sketches illustrating strike, dip, monocline, anticline, syncline, and a normal fault. (Pennsylvania Geol. & Topog. Surv.)

on the deep-sea floor, although a system of ridges and valleys like the Jura Mountains should persist almost indefinitely there since there are no changes of temperature to crack the rocks, no rivers or glaciers to wear the ridges

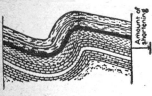 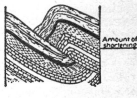

Sketches illustrating thrust faulting. (Pennsylvania Geol. & Topog. Surv.)

away, and therefore no supply of rock waste to fill up the valleys with sediment.

A more serious objection is that the amount of shrinkage needed to account for the observed folding and over-thrusting in the Alps, the Himalaya, the Appalachians and other mountain ranges of the present and the past seems to be more than the simple contraction theory requires or can account for. To increase our perplexity, the discovery that radioactive substances in the rocks are continually giving off heat has made it doubtful whether the earth is on the whole losing or gaining heat at the present time. But the discussion of these matters is so circumscribed by hypotheses, and the data are still so incompletely known, that it is best to keep an open mind. It is certain that we cannot wholly reject the contraction theory, although we may be compelled to modify it. Whatever the difficulties, contraction of the earth in cooling remains by far the most obvious and most likely cause of both vertical and horizontal movements of the crust. . . .

Rifts and Ramps

These two terms have virtually the same meaning in geology as in everyday life. A rift is an opening or parting, as when we speak of a rift in the clouds; a ramp is a mound or slope that has been thrown up, a rampart. The first involves the idea of breaking and moving apart; the second that of raising an obstruction. In geology these terms are used to describe the effects produced respectively by the sinking and by the rising of blocks of the earth's crust which are bounded by fractions. If the movement is not accompanied by fracture, the terms rift and ramp are not used. Intense folding such as we have pictured in the Alps is almost always accompanied by fracture of the rocks concerned; but the phenomena that we have now to consider are simple fracture effects and folding is subordinate or absent. A fracture along which one block of the crust has moved relatively to the other is a *fault* in geological language.

There are parts of western America and East Africa that remind one of a badly laid cement pavement. Such a pavement soon develops a network of intersecting cracks, and as the foundation settles the pavement breaks up into a lot of disconnected blocks, some of which sink as a whole below the original level of the pavement while other blocks stand high and others still are tilted, with one edge raised and the other lowered. The high plateaus of Utah, Nevada and Arizona are tilted blocks of the crust separated from one another by faults along which the vertical movement of the blocks has sometimes been as much as two miles. Of course this does not mean that the plateaus are now bounded by cliffs two miles high, for the upward or downward movement of the blocks has been as slow as all great crustal movements are; and all the time movement was going on, the agents of erosion were busy wearing down the heights and reducing the steepness of the slopes; but the outlines of the tilted blocks are still apparent in the surface relief of the region, and the amount of vertical movement can be measured by tracing particular layers from one

Section across the Sierra Nevada and Great Basin of California, to the Wasatch Mountains, Utah

block to another. Some of the uptilted blocks are still steep enough and high enough to earn the name of mountains, as in the Sierra Nevada of California and the Wasatch Mountains of Utah, but they are mountains of a very different character from those that we have already discussed. In their structure folding is quite subordinate to faulting, and what folding there is is a simple warping very different from the close wrinkles of the Appalachians and the overfolds of the Alps. The Sierra Nevada as a whole is a great warped block several hundred miles long and seventy-five miles wide, of which the eastern edge has been tilted higher than the western. The highest peaks, which are all on the eastern edge, are ten to fourteen thousand feet above sea level. The eastern face is not bounded by one fault plane but by a number of parallel planes along which the descent of five thousand feet into Owens Valley takes place step by step, giving the effect of a gigantic flight of stairs. It will readily be understood that such a gigantic crust block could hardly be raised without a good deal of internal warping, but it remains true that faulting is much more characteristic of these mountains than folding.

It is very difficult in such a case to decide whether the high blocks have risen or the low blocks have sunk, or whether both have moved, but in opposite directions. Probably the latter view is correct in most cases. It seems clear that upward and downward movements of the crust are only possible if the matter beneath the crust is in a plastic condition, that is, if there is a zone or reservoir of magma underneath. To confirm this view we find that active volcanoes, great lava fields, and intrusive sheets of igneous rock are common in regions of block faulting. The shattering of the plateau regions of Arizona and Utah was related to outpourings of lava in the Tertiary Period, and the prodigious rift and ramp movements in East Africa went hand in hand with great effusions of lava in Kenya, Uganda and Abyssinia. We have already seen that the regular arrangement of the volcanoes of the Phlegrean Fields, the Galápagos and other island groups suggests that these volcanoes have arisen at the intersections of a system of fractures.

The main faults in any region are often nearly parallel, and if movement takes place in the same direction along each of them the result is step faulting. More often there are two or more sets of faults that cross each other at angles approaching sixty or ninety degrees. The fault systems of East Africa . . . form a network of fissures running northeast and northwest, and these are cut by a third series with a northerly trend. Although the main faults in any such region fall into orderly groups, the minor faults often form a random network that defies simple description. The faulting in parts of Arizona has been said to be "only less difficult of analysis than is a pane of shattered glass."

There are in some parts of the world, both on land and on the deep-sea floor, curious trenchlike valleys with steep, nearly straight walls which irresistibly suggest that they have been formed by the sinking of a long, narrow crust block. The best example for study is the valley of the Jordan and the Dead Sea. Approaching this valley from the Mediterranean one crosses the plains of Sharon and rises gradually up to the plateau of Judea, two to three thousand feet above sea level. From here there is a sudden drop, precipitous in parts, to the bottom of the Dead Sea, two thousand, six hundred feet below the Mediterranean Sea level. East of the Dead Sea the ground again rises steeply to the Trans-Jordan plateau, which stands at about the same level as the Judean plateau. The sunken area is altogether some four hundred miles long and from ten to twenty-five miles wide, and the steep slopes or escarpments that bound it are remarkably straight and parallel. Early travelers in Palestine described the Jordan Valley as a sunken segment of the crust. They had no geological

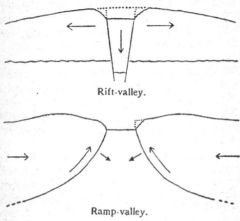

Rift-valley.

Ramp-valley.

Ideal cross-section of a rift-valley (keystone hypothesis) and a ramp-valley (Willis)

authority for their view, but they could hardly go wrong since the floor of the valley is far below sea level. A river may cut a deep, steep-sided gorge, but it cannot cut it deeper than sea level. A glacier descending to the sea will grind its way along the sea floor until it reaches water deep enough to float it, so the bottom of a glaciated valley may lie a few score feet below sea level; but there is no reason to believe that the Jordan Valley has ever been occupied by a glacier, so one must conclude that it owes its great depth to an actual sinking of the crust. Geological evidence has completely confirmed the opinion formed by early travelers, for the faults that bound the valley have been proved and traced on the map.

Such a valley is in the everyday sense of the word a

rift in the earth's crust, and geologists have become accustomed to speak of the Jordan Valley as a rift valley. To illustrate the manner in which they suppose it to have been formed they have used the simile of an arch of masonry in which the keystone has dropped out of place. The plateaus of Judea and Trans-Jordania, sloping respectively to west and to east, are the limbs of the arch; the Jordan crust block is the sunken keystone. On this hypothesis the keystone sank because the support given to it by the flanks of the arch was withdrawn and the arch was not strong enough to stand by itself. But one can also imagine a broad, flat arch failing because the pressure from the sides is too great; the central strip (we must not use the keystone analogy in this case) is forced down and partly overridden by the flanks. This process might give a similar result at the surface; but in the first case the depression would be a rift valley, for the bottom has dropped down; in the second case it would be a ramp valley, for the sides have been forced up and the depression of the bottom is a secondary matter.

It is extraordinarily difficult to decide between these two interpretations. To the layman the difference may seem to be a trifling one, but to the geologist engaged in studying the forces that have shaped the crust of the earth the difference is highly significant. It raises the question whether a section of the earth's crust can ever become wider, as an arch must do when its keystone falls in, or whether the crust is always and everywhere contracting and compression is the essential factor in originating all earth features. That question still awaits an answer. . . .

The Birth of Parícutin
By Jenaro Gonzalez and William Foshag

Many thousands of volcanoes, old and young, are scattered over the earth's surface. Some that are very old have been reduced to traces of erosion, others are still perfectly preserved in their essential form, although cold and inactive.

About five hundred volcanoes are known to have been active within historical times, although the number of volcanoes in eruption at one time is never large. With very few exceptions the active volcanoes are old and well-established features, antedating the history of man by many years, some having their beginnings a million or more years ago.

In all recorded history there have been but six instances reported of a new volcano being born, that is, originating at a spot with no evidence of previous volcanic outbursts. To these six, we can now add a seventh—Parícutin Volcano—that arose in a corn field in Mexico on February 20, 1943. The only previously recorded instance in which the outbreak of a new volcano was actually observed is that in Chinyero, Tenerife, which opened up about one hundred meters from a farmer and his son.

In the case of Parícutin Volcano, four persons actually saw its beginning at very close hand, and their observations furnish the first adequate account of this rare phenomenon. Others visited the spot after the first outbreak, and scientists were soon on hand to submit it to detailed study. Since there are so many apocryphal accounts of what took place during the first moments of Parícutin Volcano, we will quote, as accurately as possible, the narration of events as recounted to us by the actual eyewitnesses. It is remarkable that, in spite of the tremendous shock and overwhelming fear induced by this sudden apparition, there is so little apparent distortion in their observations. . . .

Before the Volcano

In the lands of Rancho Tepacua there existed for many years a small hole. Both Dionisio Pulido and his brother Dolores mentioned it as having existed all during their tenure of the land. Each year they cast dirt and debris into this cavity, but it showed no appreciable signs of becoming filled. Sra. Severiana Murilla, now an old lady, recalls how as a child, more than fifty years ago, she played about this small pit. She remembered it well for two reasons; first, because her father warned her to avoid the spot, saying that it was the entrance to an old Spanish mine (although no mining activity has been recorded in the area); and second, because one frequently heard subterranean noises, as if made by falling rocks, near the hole. Further, they amused themselves around the hole because it emitted a pleasant warmth.

Early February is the season of Barbecho, the first plowing of the year, in preparation for the season's sowing. At this time the villagers are in their fields busily engaged in their various tasks. On February 5th the first premonition of the impending disaster was noticed—the earth began to tremble. With each succeeding day the tremors increased, both in number and in violence. Subterranean noises, too, could be heard with increasing frequency and intensity. . . . These seemingly unnatural manifestations kept the inhabitants in constant turmoil and fear. The earth tremors became so frequent and so violent that it was feared the great church of Parangaricutiro, with its massive walls of masonry more than a meter thick, would collapse. As a precaution, the sacred image of the church, El Señor de las Milagros, famous throughout the region for its miraculous powers, was placed in the main plaza, near the village cross, and by a strange coincidence faced directly toward the spot where the volcano would appear.

February 20, 1943

February 20th was clear and calm. Dionisio Pulido left his village of Parícutin to prepare his farm "Cuiyútziro" for the coming sowing. With him he took his oxen and his plow. He was accompanied by his wife Paula and his son, who would watch the sheep, and Demetrio Toral (who died a short time ago in Calzontzin) to help with the plowing.

In the afternoon, after midday, I joined my wife and son, who were watching the sheep, and inquired if anything new had occurred, since for two weeks we had felt strong *temblores* in the region. Paula replied, yes, that she had heard noise and thunder underground. Scarcely had she finished speaking when I, myself, heard a noise, like thunder during a rainstorm, but I could not explain it, for the sky above was clear and the day was so peaceful, as it is in February.

At four o'clock I left my wife to set fire to a pile of branches which Demetrio and I and another, whose name I cannot remember, had gathered. I went to burn the branches when I noticed that at a *cueva*,* which was situated on one of the knolls of my farm, a fissure had opened, and I noticed that this fissure, as I followed it with my eye, was long and passed from where I stood, through the hole, and continued in the direction of the Cerro de Canijuata, where Canijuata joins the Mesa of Cocojara. Here is something new and strange, thought I, and I searched the ground for marks to see whether or not it had opened in the night but could find none; and I saw that it was a kind of fissure that had only a depth of half a meter. I set about to ignite the branches again, when I felt a thunder, the trees trembled, and I turned to speak to Paula; and it was then I saw how, in the hole, the ground swelled and raised itself—two or two and one-half meters high—and a kind of smoke or fine dust—gray, like ashes —began to rise up in a portion of the crack that I had not previously seen, near the *resumidero*. Immediately more smoke began to rise, with a hiss or whistle, loud and continuous, and there was a smell of sulfur. I then became greatly frightened and tried to help unyoke one of the ox teams. I hardly knew what to do, so stunned was I before this, not knowing what to think or what to do and not able to find my wife or my son or my animals. Finally my wits returned and I recalled the sacred Señor de los Milagros, which was in the church in San Juan (Parangaricutiro) and in a loud voice I cried: "Santo Señor de los Milagros, you brought me into this world—now save me from the dangers in which I am about to die," and I looked toward the fissure from whence rose the smoke, and my fear, for the first time, disappeared. I ran to see if I could save my family and my companions and my oxen, but I did not see them, and thought that they had taken the oxen to the spring for water. When I saw that there was no longer any water in the spring, for it was near the fissure, I thought the water was lost because of the fissure. Then, very frightened, I mounted my mare and galloped to Parícutin, where I found my wife and son and friends awaiting, fearing that I might be dead, and that they would never see me again. On the road to Parícutin I thought of my little animals, the yoke oxen, that were going to die in that flame and smoke but upon arriving at my house I was happy to see that they were there.

At no time did Pulido notice any heat in the ground about the spot. . . .

*Variously referred to by Pulido as a *cueva* (cave or grotto), *resumidero* (a hole or crevice into which water disappears during the rainy season) or *agujero* (a hole).

Aurora de Cuara, wife of Gregorio Cuaro Sota, had been with her family at their farm at San Nicolas, some twenty kilometers from Parangaricutiro. All during the day they felt very strong earth tremors and heard subterranean noises. Aurora and her children were returning afoot to Parangaricutiro along the road that leads directly past Cuiyútziro. At 4:30 P.M. they reached the foot of the Piedra del Sol, precisely at the time when the ground opened up.

As I passed the Piedra del Sol, I felt very heavy earth shocks and saw the earth open up, like a fissure. From this fissure arose a smoke of very fine gray dust to about one-half the height of the nearby pine trees.

Although terribly frightened Aurora clambered to the summit of the rock, in order that she might see what was happening. The fissure was about fifty meters distant. There was no "thunder" but she was able to see that not only smoke and gray dust, but also "sparks" rose from the fissure. She could see Pulido assist his helper unyoke the oxen but could not see Paula because a grove of pines obscured a full view of the farm, and she saw the two men flee in fright toward the village. At the Piedra del Sol, one could hear noises like a roar or like a stone falling down a deep well and striking the sides.

Dolores Pulido, brother of Dionisio, was working in the forest on Cerra de Janánboro. He saw smoke arising from his brother's land and went to see what had taken place. He reached the spot about 6 P.M. and saw, from a distance of eight meters, smoke issuing from a vent in the ground. About this vent were low mounds of fine gray dust. He was unable to approach closer because of falling stones. He then took fright and fled.

In Parangaricutiro, Luis Ortiz Solorio was standing near his house, talking to his neighbor, the shoemaker. It was a quarter past five in the afternoon. Looking toward Quitzocho, he saw a thin column of smoke arising. He went to the plaza, where many people had gathered in front of the church, for news had come that the earth had opened up and smoke was issuing from a crack in the ground. The Cura, José Caballero, with the consent of the

Presidente, Felipe Cuara Amezcua, decided to send a group of men to the spot to see what had taken place. Solorio offered to go, also Jesús Anguiano, Jesús Martinez, Antonio Escalera, and Miguel Campoverde. Since the Cura believed this mission would be a dangerous one in which they might lose their lives, and to give them spirit, as well as valor, he gave them his benediction.

They went by horse, riding rapidly, and very soon came to the spot, the first two to arrive being Jesús Anguiano and Jesús Martinez. They found that the earth had opened, forming a kind of fissure, at the extreme southern end of which was a hole about half a meter across, from which issued smoke, and red-hot stones were thrown into the air a short distance. Anguiano, desirous to see what was taking place in the hole, approached the spot, when Solorio cried out to come back, the side was about to collapse. Scarcely had he leapt back when the wall fell in, widening the orifice to two meters across, and the column of smoke increased in size.

According to Anguiano, the orifice was pear-shaped and from this cavity arose a fine gray dust like ashes and "sparks," and stones were thrown out without much force to a height of five meters. A choking odor pervaded the spot. In the vent the sand was "boiling" like the bubbling sand in a rising spring, with a noise like a large jug of water, boiling vigorously, or boulders dragged along a stream bed by a river in flood. About the vent small mounds of fine dust half a meter high had gathered. This fine ash was very hot but Anguiano collected some in his handkerchief as well as two of the hot stones.

The ground shook violently, "jumping up and down, not with the swaying motion they had experienced in Parangaricutiro."

They decided then to return and report what they had seen, and they carried with them the ash and the two stones. The stones were delivered to the Cura, and being still hot, they were placed in a dish, and the Cura exorcised them, that the volcano might cease. The Cura and others then consulted a book on Vesuvius in the library of the church, and it was decided that what they had seen was a volcano, which greatly astonished the gathered people.

Between six and nine o'clock the volcano began to throw

out large stones, and at ten o'clock, one could see clearly, from Parangaricutiro, through the pine trees, incandescent rocks hurled out, but without any thunderous noises. Between eleven o'clock and midnight the volcano began to roar, huge incandescent bombs were hurled into the air, and flashes of lightning appeared in the heavy ash column.

On the morning of February 21st, Pulido drove his oxen to the forest to graze and then went to his farm to see what had taken place. At eight o'clock the volcano was about ten meters high. It emitted smoke and hurled out hot rocks with great violence.

With the outbreak of the volcano, the earth tremors ceased, much to the relief of the populace. The Cura and Presidente allayed their fears somewhat, but on the morning of the 21st a strong earthquake threw them into panic and they abandoned their homes, those from Parícutin fleeing to Parangaricutiro, those from Parangaricutiro to Angahuan or Uruapan, and those from Angahuan to the mountains. . . .

During the morning of the 21st the activity of Parícutin Volcano greatly increased in intensity, casting out great quantities of incandescent material to build up its cone. By midday its height was variously estimated at thirty to fifty meters. The amount of ash, however, was relatively small and the eruptive column of less size and vigor than appeared some weeks later.

The first lava began to flow within two days after the initial outburst, perhaps sometime during the day of the 21st. It issued as a viscous mass, spreading slowly over the fields of Cuiyútziro and Quitzocho. It moved slowly, about five meters per hour, forming a rugged sheet of torn and jumbled lava fragments.

Later Growth

Parícutin Volcano continued to grow with startling rapidity. On February 26th it had reached a height of more than one hundred and sixty meters, and its explosive activity had increased to an awesome thunderous bombardment, in which immense quantities of viscous lava were hurled continuously into the air; the noise of these tremendous explosions could be heard in many remote corners of Michoacan, and even in Guanajuto, three hundred and fifty kilometers to the northeast.

In late March the first lava ceased flowing and the eruptive activity changed to a heavy emission of ash, the eruptive column rising to a height of more than twenty thousand feet. This ash covered the countryside for miles around, ruining the fields and destroying the forests.

In time the lavas reached both Parangaricutiro and Parícutin, engulfing and destroying them, and scattering their inhabitants to other areas. Celadonio Gutierrez wrote on February 20, 1946, in his simple diary of the life of the volcano:

Three years ago my village existed tranquilly, without any warning of the volcano as it exists today. Three years ago all parts of this region were beautiful, with fruit trees in the villages and in the fields, green pastures, beautiful lands that demonstrated the wealth of the region, with cattle and sheep, and droves of horses that grazed in the rich fields. Now there remains for me only a memory and a pride to have known it as it was three years ago.

Parícutin Volcano continued to grow, although most of the later growth was in width rather than height. The greatest height recorded in 1946 was fifteen hundred feet. . .
Parícutin became quiescent in 1952. EDS.

Rocks and Minerals

By Carey Croneis and William C. Krumbein

. . . Rocks formed by the hardening of lava are by no means rare, nor are they confined to regions in which active volcanoes now exist. . . . Large parts of the State of Idaho, for example, are covered with hardened lavas that poured from numerous vents in the dim past. No active volcanoes now exist in Idaho; but at the time of the activity, vast seas of liquid lava inundated the area, only to freeze into rigid rocks as their heat content was dissipated into the atmosphere. They are literally frozen seas of lava; and even today the rough, tumbled-about surface is much the same as it was shortly after Vulcan held his court among those barren hills.

Although these lavas hardened literally millions of years ago, there is no doubt that they once were liquid. All rocks carry with them some traces of their origin, just as sediments bear ripple marks and have bedding to attest to their origin. A common attribute of hardened lavas is a certain denseness of texture occasioned by the finely crystalline or glassy body of the rock. Fluid lava rapidly cools by radiation when it reaches the surface, and the rapid solidification that ensues results in very fine crystals or even a glassy solid. Sometimes the lava hardens while bubbles of gas are still rising to the surface, so that the bubbles become frozen into the rock. The presence of such bubbles may be an important criterion in proving that the rocks are lavas.

Not only do volcanoes pour out molten rock, but usually during explosive phases great clouds of dust and volcanic fragments are thrown into the air. These settle back to the ground, where they may become incorporated into the lavas; or they may form deposits of their own. . . .

We should pause here to clear up one or two terms that we shall need. Strictly, the word *lava* refers to liquid rock or its hardened forms on the surface of the earth. It has also been applied to liquid rock that never sees the light of day—those bodies of lava that constitute the igneous intrusions. To avoid confusion, however, we shall use the term *magma* for liquid rock beneath the surface of the earth, confining *lava* to that part which actually escapes to the surface and there hardens into the volcanic rocks.

Not only, then, are there rocks that form from the hardening of lava at the earth's surface, but also a whole series of rocks that form from the crystallization of magmas beneath the surface. Just as the lavas bear evidence of their former liquid condition, so do the intrusive igneous rocks. *It is, indeed, from the evidence that such rocks once were liquid that we infer the whole process of igneous intrusion.* It is readily possible to watch volcanic rocks form at the earth's surface, because a lava poured out on the surface may be studied in full detail a few days later. Samples of the liquid lava may even be collected, and the gases that accompany the eruption may be studied. In this manner a large body of direct evidence can be built up. No one, however, has ever seen a deep-seated magma solidify, so that here we must rely on indirect evidence.

There is one main attribute of the intrusive igneous rocks that differs from those of the hardened lavas, and that is the size of the crystals. Lavas generally do not have crystals large enough to be seen clearly with the unaided eye, while the intrusive rocks seldom have crystals too small to be seen as distinct entities. The hardened surface lavas range from volcanic glass (which has no crystals at all) to dense rocks that show innumerable glints to the eye from myriads of tiny crystals. When the latter are studied under the microscope, it is found that the minerals present may be identical with those in the coarser-grained intrusive rocks. Furthermore, the crystals in intrusive rocks show a continuous gradation in size from the tiny crystals of dikes and sills to the large crystals of batholithic intrusions. In a similar fashion, the chemical compositions of the rocks furnish striking evidence of the essential similarity of the two kinds of rocks. It is possible to find hardened lavas with chemical compositions essentially identical with those of certain deep-seated rocks. Thus in many series of rocks from lavas to coarse intrusives, the only major difference seems to be one of crystal size. What may we conclude from this? Simply, that both the surface lavas and the intrusives of the series had a common origin but differed in the environment of their solidification.

When a lava is poured on the surface, the loss of heat is extremely rapid because of the much lower temperature of the air and the large surface area of the lava sheet, so that it tends to solidify rapidly. With rapid solidification comes a tendency toward minute crystals, because the growth of crystals requires a gradual change of conditions, rather than an abrupt one. Allow the body of magma to remain deeply buried, however, and the loss of heat is much slower. This is due to the heated condition of the surrounding rocks themselves, as well as their poor thermal conductivity. Among the larger intrusions there is often relatively less surface area, also. That there is some loss of heat is attested by the geothermal gradient, which shows that heat is slowly being radiated out into space by the earth as a whole. Hence the magma will gradually cool, but so gradually that in terms of human comparisons it may appear to be infinitely slow. A million years? Perhaps; but at any rate, long enough for all the magma to crystallize completely into crystals, often of considerable size.

It is from reasoning like this that we infer the origin of coarsely crystalline rocks from bodies of magma deeply buried and slowly cooling. Here again is an example of adjustment to environment, and the tendency toward states of equilibrium. If we can clearly understand that these two broad classes of igneous rocks, the extrusives and the intrusives, are products of environments, the details of classification become quite simple. If we were inclined to the use of tables, it would be possible to contrast the two environments and their results something like this:

SURFACE CONDITIONS	DEEP BURIAL
Rapid radiation of heat content	Relative insulation from loss of heat
Low pressures	High pressures
Small crystals or none	Large crystals usual

. . . One of the most fertile lines of inquiry among the coarse-grained rocks is a study of the crystals themselves. It may seem surprising, but it is nevertheless true, that even the order in which the crystals appeared can be determined, even though the rocks may have crystallized millions of years ago.

Suppose we stop along the way here and see just how the crystals of igneous rocks are studied and what they tell us about the process of solidification of the magma. Consider a liquid magma which will form several minerals as it cools. Each of these minerals will have its own properties, and consequently will behave differently from the others. We may accordingly expect that, as the temperature drops, the minerals will not crystallize simultaneously, but rather a combination of solubility and concentration will largely determine which crystals appear first. These first crystals to appear will be bounded by plane crystal faces because nothing interferes with their complete growth. The same may be true of the second mineral; but as the liquid becomes nearly filled with crystals, later arrivals must adapt themselves to somewhat constricted surroundings. The later crystals may therefore have only some of their faces developed; or conceivably they may have none, but must form the interstices among the earlier crystals. Furthermore, the earlier crystals may be imbedded in later crystals which simply grow around them, so that the final result is a close interlocking of all the minerals present.

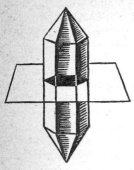

Crystal sections

Now, in the igneous rocks we use these principles in determining the sequence in which the several minerals formed. A slice of the rock, ground down to extreme thinness, is studied under the microscope. These thin sections are essentially in two dimensions; they are so thin that they are quite transparent. Hence we usually do not see the entire crystals but only sections through them. However, when we cut through a solid bounded by plane faces, the resulting section is an area bounded by straight lines, as the adjoining diagrams show.

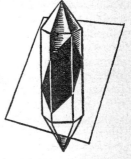

. . . The deep-seated igneous rocks are composed of primary minerals . . . and these include the ferromagnesians, the feldspars and quartz. Suppose we choose a rock that contains all three minerals. *Granite* is such a rock; and when we study a thin section of it under the microscope, we find that the order of crystallization shows that the first minerals to appear (except for various minor constituents that do not concern us) were the ferromagnesians. These, for the most part, are bounded by crystal faces. The next minerals that form are the feldspars, and finally the quartz fills in the spaces between the earlier crystals. . . .

Interesting as this may be, it is only the beginning of the story. This *order of crystallization,* as it is called, tells us a lot more. It tells us, in fact, something about the chemical reactions that probably took place in the magma before or while it cooled. To develop this point we shall have to recall some . . . things . . . about the chemical composition of the primary minerals. Remember that the quartz is crystallized silicon oxide, SiO_2, and that the ferromagnesians and feldspars are silicates, and so have silicon oxide, or silica, in their chemical make-up. Now if the ferromagnesians crystallize first, that must mean that some of the silica in the original melt first unites with the iron oxides and the magnesian oxide (plus a few others) to form the ferromagnesians. Next, more of the silica must combine with the oxides of aluminum, calcium, sodium and potassium, to form the various feldspars. After all of these oxides have combined with some of the silica, then the *excess silica crystallizes out as quartz.*

We have almost leaned over backward to make this story simple. . . . The sequence given includes the salient features of the story. Granite, we see, is a rock with a high percentage of silica in its ultimate chemical composition — so much so, that after all the other oxides have combined with it, there still is some silica left to crystallize out as quartz.

Now, although granite has a fairly high silica content and a relatively low content of iron and magnesium oxides, it is only one of a large number of coarsely crystalline igneous

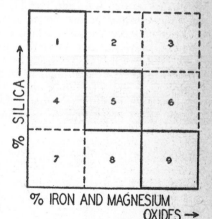

Diagram of possible igneous rock types. The total silica is contrasted against total iron and magnesium oxides. The other oxides are not included

rocks. . . . The *normal series* of igneous rocks . . . includes three types. To bring this point out, we may say that from a chemical standpoint it is possible to contrast the percentage of silica in the rock with the combined percentages of iron and magnesium oxides. That is, we may find rocks low both in silica and in iron-magnesium oxides, or we may find them rich in one and low in the other. Look at the adjacent diagram and notice that the vertical axis shows the total amount of silica in the rock and that the horizontal axis shows the total amount of iron and magnesium oxides. We have arbitrarily divided the area into nine squares, and have numbered them. At a glance we may see that square No. 1, for example, has much silica and little iron-magnesium oxide; No. 9 has little silica and much iron-magnesium oxide; and so on. Thus we find in nature that all sorts of rocks are possible; but fortunately, most igneous rocks fall into three of the squares, which we have outlined more heavily. As you may notice, they form a diagonal of our chart; which means that from rocks high in silica and low in iron-magnesium oxides they descend to rocks high in iron-magnesium oxides and low in silica. It is this series that we shall examine. As a starter, we may say that granite is the typical rock of square No. 1.

Since granite has quite a high percentage of silica, we may call it an *acidic rock,* because silicon oxide is an acidic oxide. Likewise the square on the lower right, being high in iron and magnesium oxides and low in silica, is called *basic,* and the middle square is called *intermediate.* The table below shows more explicitly how the rocks within these three squares vary in their percentages of the oxides. . . .

Rock Type	Percentage of Silica	Percentage of Iron-Magnesium Oxides	Percentage of All Other Oxides
Acidic	70	3	27
Intermediate	57	12	31
Basic	48	17	35

Now, from the relation between the percentages of silica and of iron-magnesium oxides in this normal series, what may we anticipate about the presence of quartz in the basic rocks? Well, if the amount of silica in their chemical make-up is relatively so low, maybe there will be no free silica left after the silicates are formed, so that no quartz can crystallize out. This is exactly the case. The basic rocks of the normal series do not contain quartz and, in extreme cases of our series, may not even form the feldspars. In that case they are practically all ferromagnesian minerals. On the same basis the intermediate rocks, with their intermediate amount of silica, may not have any quartz present; but they do have enough silica to form the feldspars, and thus they consist largely of ferromagnesians and feldspar. If we summarize all these data, we find that a table emerges from the welter of material presented:

ORDER OF CRYSTALLIZATION AND MINERALS
PRESENT IN THE DEEP-SEATED IGNEOUS ROCKS
OF THE NORMAL SERIES

Acidic Rocks	*Intermediate Rocks*	*Basic Rocks*
Ferromagnesians	Ferromagnesians	Ferromagnesians
Feldspars	Feldspars	(May have feldspars)
Quartz	(May have some quartz)	No quartz

As we pass from the acidic to the basic rocks, the diminished amount of silica in the original magma reflects itself by the absence of the minerals with high silica contents. . . .

Now that we are getting acquainted with these rocks, it may be interesting to know their names. The acidic rocks are *granites,* the intermediate rocks are *diorites,* and the basic rocks are *gabbros.*

But these, remember, are the deep-seated, coarsely crystalline rocks of the normal series. We said that each of the chemical types occurred in two kinds: the hardened surface lavas and the deep-seated igneous rocks in our series, so there are three parallel groups of surface lavas. Each pair belongs to the same chemical category but differs in the environment of cooling. We may accordingly put all of our rocks in a single table, which will then afford us a classification of these igneous rocks.

Environment	*Acidic*	*Intermediate*	*Basic*
Surface (small crystals)	Rhyolite	Andesite	Basalt
Deep-seated (large crystals)	Granite	Diorite	Gabbro

The extrusive equivalent of granite, *rhyolite,* is light in color, whereas *basalt,* the extrusive equivalent of gabbro, is quite dark. As we may anticipate, *andesite* is intermediate in appearance. All three of these surface igneous rocks are fine-grained.

We may see the significance of the whole story now at a glance. The table tells us that if a volume of magma rich in silica rises from within the earth, and actually reaches the surface as lava, the rapid cooling will result in rhyolite being formed; while if the magma does not escape, but hardens underground, a coarsely crystalline granite will result. And so on for the other types. Naturally enough, there are many individual species of rocks that we have not mentioned because of their relative rarity. Our simple classification tells the fundamentals of the story, and further details merely embellish and complicate it. . . .

There is, however, one peculiar type of igneous rock that deserves mention, because it bears evidence of having cooled in two environments. Sometimes a body of magma is intruded beneath the surface and there begins its cooling until a few of the earlier crystals have appeared in the still largely liquid magma. Later on, renewed activity may force this magma upward toward the surface. Here it cools more rapidly. The kind of rock that forms is easy to predict. It will be one in which some large crystals are embedded in a fine-grained or glassy groundness. Such a rock is called *porphyry*. Any of our three chemical types of rock may have a porphyritic phase, since that is controlled entirely by environment and is independent of composition.*

It may be interesting now to consider why there are these several chemical types of igneous rocks, but at most we can only touch upon the subject. Apparently, a whole series of complicated adjustments to environment on the part of the deeply buried magma results in a separation of parts of the magma during cooling. Among the many factors that may be operative is one that stands out prominently. Imagine a slowly cooling magma of about the composition of an intermediate or a basic igneous rock. The earliest crystals to form are the ferromagnesians; and these crystals, having a rather high density, tend to settle downward in the still liquid magma. In the course of time they gradually concentrate toward the bottom, and this leaves the top of the magma relatively more concentrated

---

* Even the rarer rocks that we are not discussing here may occur as porphyry. In that case the first large crystals that form may not be ferromagnesians or even feldspar.

in the other oxides, which tend to form feldspars and quartz. If now the liquid portion is squeezed out by diastrophic processes, it may lead ultimately to igneous rocks of a more acidic nature. Thus the normal series of rocks tends to be formed. . . .

Our story of the igneous rocks is nearly finished, although actually we have hardly glanced at the subject. Further detail involves great complexity, because nature is seldom as simple as the pictures we draw. . . . We must still take up one other great group of rocks, which in complexity easily parallels the igneous rocks. . . .

Heredity versus Environment

A palimpsest is a document that had its writing erased so that the parchment could be used again. Traces of the earlier words may possibly be discerned, however; and the historian, poring over the musty parchment, may bring to light startling and important data. Just so the geologist, bending over his microscope, studies rocks for evidences of their earlier histories. The fruitfulness of this search was demonstrated by the study of igneous rocks. In like manner, the debris from the weathering of crystalline rocks may contain traces of the original minerals, from which the nature of the parent rock can be determined.

An even wider field for this search is among a large class of rocks so altered by environmental conditions that the original rock may never be identified. Heredity may thus yield almost completely to the irresistible impact of environment. . . .

Processes of sedimentation are taking place practically continuously, and sediments now beneath the seas will later be buried beneath other sediments, and so *ad infinitum*. As the load of overlying sediments increases, the earlier materials are squeezed and compressed by the increasing overburden. They are, in other words, entering a new environment. Just as deep-seated igneous rocks undergo alterations to weathered debris when erosion exposes them at the surface, so the debris itself, laid down as sediments, undergoes a new cycle of changes due to removal from surface conditions—changes that return to the material some of the original deep-seated characteristics.

Among the first changes that take place are a greater compaction of the particles, a cementation of the loose grains into a coherent rock, and the chemical alteration of some of the clayey minerals to new chemical compounds. Thus muds become shales, sands change to sandstones, and gravels to conglomerates. In short, they have entered the domain of the *indurated* or hardened sedimentary rocks. To all these changes we may apply the term *metamorphism,* or *a change in form;* but it is metamorphism in its gentlest and mildest state. The pressures are predominately static, that is, they depend merely on the overburden of the later rocks; and what rise of temperature there may be is not excessive.

There are other and more dynamic aspects of metamorphism, and to them we shall devote most of our discussion. Here are included some deep-seated environmental changes of such magnitude that the rock may be wholly altered; its physical appearance may be completely changed, and in some cases its chemical composition as well. Such highly altered rocks are called *metamorphic rocks,* and they constitute the third and last great group. Metamorphic rocks arise from either sedimentary or igneous rocks, in environments where stability or equilibrium demands a complete alteration of the parent rock in the direction of greater density, both physical and chemical.

An example will help to crystallize our notions. Suppose a body of magma is introduced into a series of sediments, deeply buried beneath the surface. The great heat content of the magma will be conducted outward through the confining rocks and will accordingly raise their temperatures. Furthermore, the gases and vapors contained within the magma will penetrate the pores of the surrounding sediments and may there enter into chemical reactions with the minerals composing them. If the surrounding rock happens to be limestone, profound alteration may take place.

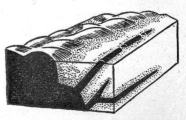

The zone of contact-metamorphosed rocks about an igneous intrusion

The heat of the intrusion will facilitate chemical reactions, and the silica contained in the hot magmatic liquids will promptly react with some of the calcite to form calcium silicates. The other constituents of the fluids will simultaneously develop a whole series of special minerals adjacent to the contact between magma and surrounding rock. Thus may arise valuable ore deposits. In addition, the physical appearance of the remaining limestone will itself change, because under the influence partly of heat it recrystallizes into a sugary rock familiar to all as *marble*.

Again we must point out that these events transpire without human witnesses, but detailed studies of the results of intrusions clearly indicate the sequence of events. We would expect the temperature to decrease away from the magma, and the magmatic liquids to diminish in chemical activity as they penetrate farther and farther into the sediments. These expectations are borne out by observation. The greatest alteration is near the contact between the limestone and the magma (when studied, of course, the magma has become a coarse-grained igneous rock); and as the limestone is followed away from the contact, the alterations gradually decrease. Indeed, from the characteristics of the new minerals formed during the metamorphism, it is possible, in a qualitative way at least, to sketch the decrease in temperature as one moves away from the contact. This is because certain minerals are known to occur only in restricted temperature ranges, and they thus furnish us with a *geological thermometer,* as it were, that enables us to evaluate the conditions extant during the metamorphism. Other lines of evidence also converge to the same conclusion, namely, that intruded bodies of magma induce profound effects in the surrounding rocks. In general the most striking changes are confined to a local area about the magmatic body, and seldom do the effects penetrate very many miles into the adjacent rock. Such metamorphism as this is called *contact metamorphism,* in distinction to more widespread metamorphic changes that partake of a regional nature. We shall come to them later.

When we analyze contact metamorphism in environmental terms, we see that the magma brings along with it a new set of conditions: a higher temperature and a whole swarm of new chemical compounds. Under the impact of these new conditions, the adjacent sediments cannot remain indifferent. Rises in temperature may in some cases cause a reorganization of the sedimentary particles into new crystals; and in some cases the minerals of the sediments may themselves not be stable in the new chemical environment. When that is so, new minerals are formed which are stable. As we may expect, however, some minerals remain relatively unaffected under almost any conditions, and among them the outstanding example is quartz. A sandstone composed of pure quartz grains may show little change due to the increased temperature; whereas limestone, we saw, is markedly effected; and shale is also changed to a considerable extent.

Even dikes and sills cause some contact metamorphism, but to a much lesser degree than large intrusions. This is due to their smaller volume, and to their relatively larger surface area, which enable the heat to be dissipated more rapidly. Thus the conditions for a prolonged series of physical and chemical changes are not present. For *time* itself is an important element in metamorphism, and the time element may be easily as important as heat or pressure in the final result.

The time element may be illustrated by considering the effect of pressure on blocks of rock. If a block of rock is struck a smart blow with a sledge hammer, it fractures and shatters. Here a great force has been applied suddenly. If, on the other hand, the rock is deeply buried, and thus subjected to great pressure on all sides, it may yield by a process other than fracture if it is subsequently acted on by diastrophic forces. The yielding in such cases is similar to a plastic flow, but it involves physical and chemical changes as well. The exact changes that take place may most conveniently be studied among the rocks in nature, where the time element may have been thousands of years and the pressure thousands of pounds to the square inch. . . . Diastrophic forces operate during mountain making, and consequently we may look for our evidence among rocks that were involved in these major upheavals of the earth's surface.

As one approaches a mountain range, he may first ride over a wide plain built up of sediments carried down by mountain streams, and finally enter the foothills of the range. These foothills are composed of stratified rocks turned up on edge; they are the marginal rocks involved in the up-bulge of the range. As our traveler enters the mountain valleys proper, he may see further traces of these same rocks, but here they have been highly contorted and folded, or mashed and shattered, by the terrific forces of Nature. Even the appearance of the rock changes, and a particular layer that in the foothills is a shale, for example, may be traced continuously into a shiny, glistening rock with a wavy, banded appearance. Here, certainly, is a high degree of alteration, and we are interested in learning how it came about. In attacking the problem of the changes that took place in the shale, we may reason this way: if the shale originally had a fairly uniform composition, then the changes that progressively take place from the foot-hills into the mountains ought to be due primarily to changes in environment. Thus, from the mountain struc-tures as a whole we may be able to learn something about the environment of folding; and by combining this knowl-edge with a study of the alterations that took place in the rock, we should be able to evaluate the one in terms of the other.

Thousands of studies have been made on such meta-morphosed rocks, and certain general conclusions regard-ing the problem have been developed. In this type of metamorphism we are dealing with much greater forces than in the case of contact phenomena, and the greater areas affected give to this aspect of the subject the name *regional metamorphism*. The changes that take place in rocks under the stresses of regional metamorphism are quite complex, and we cannot stop to detail them all. Rather, we shall content ourselves with the transforma-tions that take place in a shaly type of rock, since it illus-trates all the principles we shall need.

Sediments, like all other rocks, have a multitude of gradations; and it is not unusual to find them intermediate between shales and sandstones or shales and limestones. Suppose we choose a sandy shale for an example, so that we have more than one mineral to deal with in our story. Sandy shales are usually composed primarily of quartz grains and clay particles. Now imagine this rock subjected to the pressure of overlying sediments, to a reasonably high temperature, and finally to the directed stresses of mountain-building forces. These mountain-building forces operate mainly from certain directions, so that there will be a direction of maximum stress and one of least stress. We shall assume the simplest case, in which there is no tendency toward rotation. Then the direction of least stress will lie in a plane at right angles to the direction of greatest pressure. In the diagram . . . the line *AB* indicates the directed diastrophic stress; and the plane of maximum relief, *CDEF,* is perpendicular to it and contains the lines of least stress. Sometimes some particular direction within this plane affords the maximum relief from the forces. That may depend on the local conditions. In any event, the great pressures tend to compress the rock into a smaller volume, but it already has been compacted by the over-lying rocks. What will happen then? Well, by recombining its elements into denser chemical compounds, the rock may have its volume reduced somewhat; and by developing new crystals oriented along the plane of maximum relief, the situation may be eased still further. Curiously enough, the adjustment of the rock to its new environment involves these very things.

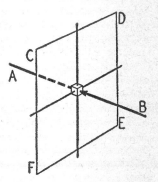

Block of rock under directed diastrophic forces

One of the first effects of regional metamorphism is a recrystallization of the original minerals into denser varieties, and among the new minerals is usually an abundance of light-colored mica. Here we may pause for a moment to introduce one more group of minerals, the *light micas,* which we have not met before. They form a group of their own for our purposes, and they are of considerable importance in the metamorphic rocks. The micas are silicates of quite complex structure; one of them, *muscovite,* or common insulating mica, has the formula $(HK)_2Al_2 (SiO_4)_3$, or $K_2O.Al_2O_3 3SiO_2.H_2O$, a complex hydrated silicate of potassium and aluminum. It is a silicate mineral, just as the feldspars and ferromagnesians are; but it belongs to a different group which, up to now, we have not had to use. Sometimes light mica occurs in igneous or sedimentary rocks. The light micas are formed largely from the clay minerals by a dehydration process during metamorphism. That is, a certain amount of chemically combined water is driven off from the clays, and the more compact and crystallized micas result.

There is an interesting thing about the micas that you may not know. That is that they may be split into very thin sheets or flakes. This property is a significant one among the metamorphic rocks. The crystals and flakes of mica that grow in the rock tend to orient their broadest dimensions in the plane of maximum relief, something like the sketch alongside. Now as the pressures continue, or even increase (remember that mountain making is a dynamic process), these mica flakes and crystals tend to separate into even thinner sheets along the plane of minimum stress. In this way the rock is able to adjust itself to the stresses of its environment and to come into balance with it by a complete internal rearrangement of its constituents. In the meantime the quartz grains are shattered into bits and strung along the same directions as the mica flakes.

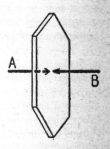

The broad dimensions of the mica are oriented normal to the stress

The net result is a rock which may easily be split along planes parallel to the direction of growth of the mica flakes. We say, accordingly, that the rock is *cleavable*. From our analysis it follows *that the cleavage of the rock tends to be at right angles to the compressive forces*. This is important, because in reading the history of folded areas the directions of cleavage in the metamorphosed rocks help us to determine the directions from which the operating stresses came. Obviously, this cleavage may develop at any angle to the bedding planes of the sedimentary rocks.

We may now pause for breath while we tell you that during the metamorphism of a shale, it first becomes *slate,* which is familiar to all as roofing material. Slate is in the stage of development where cleavage is prominent. That is why slate may so readily be split into thin slabs. In a later stage of metamorphism, when the micas become predominant, the rock becomes a *mica schist,* which is a light-colored rock with a glistening appearance due to the myriads of tiny mica flakes distributed through it. Schist also tends to split somewhat readily along the surface in which the mica flakes lie.

We have purposely kept our story simple. In nature it is infinitely complicated. For accompanying the metamorphism of the rocks themselves there may be a folding of the entire series of beds into a mountain chain. These events may require thousands of years, and the reader should remember that what we find among the eroded mountains are only the end products of these long and complicated processes. By a careful comparison of chemical compositions, by a study of the gradations among the metamorphic rocks, and by inferential reasoning, the story that we have presented has been built up. Moreover, new techniques of analysis are continually being developed to solve the infinitely complex problems of the metamorphic rocks. Modern methods involve the very grains and crystals of the rock, and their exact orientations in space. Optical methods and X-rays may be used in this work; and the net effect is that the very *fabric* of the rock is determined, from which much is learned concerning the nature of metamorphic adjustments. These newer techniques illustrate the wide diversity of methods used by geologists in reaching their conclusions. The emphasis throughout is ultimately upon *environment, because the conditions to which the rocks are subjected determine the kind of metamorphic changes that occur.*

The energy involved in these metamorphic changes probably has something to do with the story. Certainly in the formation of metamorphic rocks, potential chemical energy is stored in the new minerals that develop. Our chemically minded readers will understand by this that metamorphic reactions are *endothermic.* In fact, many deep-seated silicate minerals contain potential chemical energy, and thus some of the earth's internal energy is locked up in the deep-seated rocks. When, later, the rocks are subjected to exposure and decay, this energy is again released.

The terms "heat" and "pressure" also loom large in any discussion of metamorphism. These two factors of the environment are perhaps the most important, although the composition of the original rocks, the new chemical compounds introduced, and time itself play their parts in the complete story. We obviously cannot pursue each of these variables in any detail if we ever expect to finish our chapter.

Even as it is, we have not mentioned the metamorphism of the igneous rocks at all. As a matter of fact, they too become metamorphosed under suitable conditions; and we may mention, as a single example, that when granite is subjected to a set of conditions similar to those we postulated for the shale, it also becomes metamorphosed, and yields a banded rock called *gneiss*.

Gneiss, showing its banded appearance, about ⅓ size. Old woodcut from Lyell, 1855

We may now summarize these metamorphic rocks in a sort of table which indicates for you the original rocks and their metamorphosed equivalents:

Sandstone → Quartzite
Shale → Slate → Mica schist
Limestone → Marble
Granite → Gneiss

These metamorphic rocks are mainly those that result from regional metamorphism. We shall not introduce the specialized types that follow in the wake of contact metamorphism, because they are not as common as the others. Marble, you will notice, is included in the list; it happens to be one of several kinds of rocks that tend to be formed under both conditions. *Quartzite* is the only one of these rocks that we have not mentioned in detail. It is an example of the effect of original composition on the final metamorphic product. The quartz grains in sandstone are so indifferent to chemical reactions, and the number of elements present (silicon and oxygen) is so limited, that the sandstone may not greatly change during metamorphism. Usually it becomes harder and more dense, owing to cementation of the grains by silicious solutions. The net effect is a rock even more quartzlike in appearance. . . .

In general, there is a tendency for the metamorphic rocks to be visibly crystalline in appearance, even when the parent rock is quite fine-grained. Thus marble is usually coarsely crystalline, whereas limestone may be rather dense in appearance. Hence the metamorphic rocks, as well as the igneous rocks, are included among the *crystalline rocks*. . . . The *fragmental rocks,* on the other hand, are composed of sediments only.

Near the beginning . . . we mentioned quite an opposite aspect to the story of metamorphism. Instead of passing into environments of greater pressure and heat, we said, rocks may enter regions of lessened pressure and lower temperatures, as when they are exposed to weathering and erosion. Under these circumstances the rocks tend to break down. From one point of view, then, we may think of rock changes as being either *constructive* or *destructive*—constructive when the rock is further compacted and recrystallized, destructive when it decomposes and decays. Thus it is possible to look at all rock processes as cyclical phenomena in which the products are the results of the particular environments in which the rocks find themselves. . . .

The Formation of Mineral Deposits
By C. C. Furnas

. . . Living organisms are not ordinarily given the proper amount of credit for their part in forming the character of the earth's surface. We ordinarily think that the inconspicuous blobs of living matter, which we see everywhere we go, run through a certain life cycle, produce progeny, die, and leave the surroundings very much the same as they were before. This picture most decidedly is not correct. An individual coral polyp does not change the character of the earth very much, but polyps in numbers of astronomical size build reefs and islands of very pure limestone. To the casual observer it would seem that the polyp has built these great masses of land out of nothing; but, of course, it cannot do that any more than man can. It has taken the calcium compounds from a very dilute solution of sea water and built up a shell of calcium compounds to protect itself. In this process of following its preordained metabolic ritual, it has concentrated calcium by several thousandfold in the form of an insoluble compound. Insignificant as the coral polyp may appear, it is one of the most important creatures in changing the character of the earth's surface.

The simple organisms which make coral islands are only a few of the millions of species that exist on the earth. Practically all these species are imbued with the single purpose of living as long as possible and producing as many progeny as possible. But inevitably tied up with all of these processes of juggling organic compounds through a life cycle there are certain phenomena of mineral metabolism. No organism exists without some metal compounds in the structure; and in nearly all cases the concentration of the essential metal in the organism is considerably higher than that in the immediate environment. Thus there are a great many possibilities for the concentration of the metallic minerals.

If you think that the feeble efforts of plants and animals can hardly be significant in shaping the mineral character of the earth, you should recall that life in some form or another has been scattered over the crust for probably a billion years, that it has been concentrating metals all during that period. You may further visualize the magnitude of their work if you are reminded that there are probably 10^{13} tons of living matter (both plant and animal) on the surface of the earth today. If that same amount of living matter had existed on the earth for only half a billion years and if the average life cycle were one year, then the total amount of living matter which has been engaged in this concentrating process would amount to 5×10^{21} tons.

This figure is approximately equal to the entire weight of the earth and one hundred and seventy times the weight of what is considered to be the earth's crust. Since the organisms have worked close to the surface, their total effect on concentrating minerals has been enormous. . . .

The mere presence of an enormous amount of organic matter would not, in itself, aid in the deposition of the minerals unless mineral concentration were going on in the organisms themselves. Investigations have shown that, in the cases of some metals, organisms have enormous powers of concentration. . . .

From the data on the quantity of matter going through the cycle of life each year and its ability to concentrate mineral elements, it is evident that plants and animals may very well have been major contributing factors in building up billions of tons of mineral deposits. Many deposits of prosphates, of silica in the form of diatomaceous earth, of copper, iron, zinc, sulphur, arsenic, iodine and vanadium have been accumulated by living organisms.

It does not necessarily follow that, because an organism concentrates a metal within its own structure, this same concentration will carry over into the immediate earthy surroundings after the organism has died; but it usually happens that way. Either the metal is tied up as an insoluble compound in the animal's skeletal structure, as in the case of the coral, or the organisms themselves congregate in such dense communities that the mineral remains build up deposits of considerable magnitude. A great many of the low animals which live in the sea drop to the bottom of the ocean as sediment when they die. The organic part of their make-up is disposed of by the ever present scavengers or by simple oxidation, but the sediments usually remain on the ocean floor. Hence, after an ocean recedes or when the crust of the earth rises, the concentrated metal compounds on the ocean floor become mineral deposits on dry land. This means that the sediments of the ocean have been enriched in certain elements by the depletion of sea water in these same constituents. . . .

A few examples of the intensity of these concentrating processes will forestall the idea that they may be insignificant. Oysters commonly build up a concentration of copper two hundredfold greater than that of sea water. As a matter of fact, nearly all the lower marine organisms concentrate copper. This is because the respiratory fluid of their bodies, which corresponds to our blood, is hemocyanin. Hemocyanin is a close chemical relative of the hemoglobin of our blood, wherein copper is used instead of iron in the essential chemical compound. Ordinary kelp is known to build up relatively high concentrations of both potassium and iodine. The lobster has a concentration of iodine in its interior structure which is several hundred thousand times that of sea water. The unattractive sea cucumber contains up to 10 per cent of vanadium in its respiratory tract. This is a concentration of many thousandfold over that of sea water. . . .

Chile saltpeter (sodium nitrate) is considered to be of organic origin. It is generally thought to have been derived from guano, bacteria or seaweed, though some contend that it is of volcanic origin. Quite likely it is a combination of all of these.

Some of the greatest iron-ore deposits of the world are generally considered to be of organic origin. An important factor in the laying down of the Clinton hematite (the iron ores of Birmingham, Alabama, Chattanooga, Tennessee, and central New York) seems to have been the presence of certain iron bacteria. In the process of formation of this ore the leaching water contained iron in suspension or solution. These bacteria gargled iron water; it was essential to their life processes. The water passed on, but the skeletons of the organisms with their high iron content stayed behind.

The greatest mineral result of biological activity is seen in the formation of coal, petroleum and oil shale. All three are derived from biological materials.

Perhaps a quarter of a billion years ago the earth was in the midst of the Carboniferous Period. Plants grew with a rapidity and luxuriance not rivaled anywhere today, even in the tropics. Over three thousand different plant species have been identified in the fossil remains of coal. More than 90 per cent of them were similar to plants we know today. The Lycopods, which are mainly small shrubs today, attained a height of a hundred feet and a diameter of three feet. Rushes were common and sometimes grew ninety feet tall. . . .

The heaviest growths occurred in extensive swamps, perhaps bordering on the flat shores of the sea. As the plants died the leaves and trunks sank onto the miry ooze of the swamp out of contact with the air. The growing cycle went on above them, year after year, century after century, until the organic debris in the bottom of the swamps was sometimes hundreds of feet thick. Climate changed, no one knows why, sediment was washed in on top of the bogs, the organic detritus was buried deeper and deeper. No oxygen penetrated the mass, so the dead plants could not decay in the conventional manner. They lay there under the ground for millions of years. We now bore into those swamp beds of the past and find—coal.

At one time it was only possible to guess about what happened in the old swamp beds during the past quarter-billion years; but the researches in organic chemistry and bacteriology have clarified the history of coal to a certain extent. It is quite evident that the principal feature of the formation of coal from plant materials consisted of the removal of oxygen from the plant structure by means of chemical or bacteriological action, or both.

The bulk of the dry substance of plants is cellulose and lignin, both of which have the generalized formula $C_6 H_{10} O_5$. In such a substance the carbon is 44.4 per cent, the hydrogen 6.2 per cent, and the oxygen 49.4 per cent by weight. As plant material changed to coal it went through various stages of decomposition, giving products which are now roughly classified as those of peat, lignite, sub-bituminous coal, bituminous coal, semi-bituminous coal, semi-anthracite, and anthracite. . . .

If one follows the life line of coal as evidenced by the content of hydrogen, carbon and oxygen, it is quite evident that oxygen was removed as the coal-forming process progressed. The oxygen removal probably was effected by the formation of carbon dioxide (CO_2) and water (H_2O). This, of course, required the removal of a certain amount of carbon and hydrogen as well. But each pound of oxygen leaving as carbon dioxide would remove only 0.375 pounds of carbon, and each pound of oxygen leaving as water would remove only 0.125 pounds of hydrogen. It is quite evident, then, that if the oxygen of the plant structure went into carbon dioxide and water and if these two substances were subsequently removed, the solid material left behind would display a net gain in the proportions of hydrogen and carbon. There is ample evidence that the gases, carbon monoxide (CO) and methane (CH_4), were also formed. Methane is evidently a common product of the decomposition of submerged vegetation. It is the common marsh gas which bubbles up from the bottom of swamps.

What caused these chemical reactions to take place in the forming of coal? There are various micro-organisms that are anaerobic; they obtain the oxygen for their living processes from the oxygen in chemical compounds rather than from the free oxygen of the air. It is generally agreed that such micro-organisms played a part in the formation of coal. Buried in the depth of the fibrous residues, they robbed the woody material of its oxygen to make water, carbon dioxide and a few other gases. Along with, or subsequent to, the organisms' action there may have been inanimate chemical actions resulting in the breaking up of oxygen compounds. Such reactions have been carried out in the laboratory. High pressures and slightly elevated temperatures, such as would be found in the coal beds, may have aided the progress of such reactions. All the reactions were very slow; but a hundred million years is a long time, long enough to allow the slowest imaginable reactions to go to completion.

The origin of petroleum is much more a matter of dispute than the origin of coal. The opinion of the experts now tips the balance in favor of a vegetable origin for petroleum, though animal life may have contributed something. Petroleum deposits seem to be associated with salt water (coal deposits were usually laid down under fresh water). The petroleum-forming situation of the past would seem to call for an extensive array of shallow seashore areas where there was a heavy growth of seaweed, diatoms and algae. The plants died and contributed their remains to the bottom ooze. There may have been considerable animal remains laid down in the same area. Some of these lower plants, such as the algae, have oil in their internal structure while they are still alive. If a great mass of these minute organisms were collected in one place and if the oil were squeezed out of each one, an oil accumulation would be started without any subsequent chemical or biological reaction.

Since it is well established that some organisms, such as the diatoms, produce oil in their own metabolic processes, it might seem sufficient to allow the matter of the explanation of the origin of petroleum to rest there; but the investigators have not been entirely satisfied with the sufficiency of that explanation. It is assumed, and with fairly good evidence, that after the plant and animal organisms had ceased to live, their bodies were worked on by anaerobic micro-organisms (perhaps similar to those instrumental in the formation of coal) which removed the oxygen to form gases and water and left behind a hydrocarbon residue which is petroleum. There is also good laboratory evidence that some of the chemical changes may have taken place without the aid of organisms.

The process of deoxidation in the case of petroleum would have to be carried much further than in the case of bituminous coal. The analysis of a typical Pennsylvania crude oil is carbon 84.9 per cent, hydrogen 13.7 per cent, and oxygen 1.4 per cent by weight. There is no adequate explanation why the residual products should be oils instead of solids, such as coal. The difference might be due to the fact that organisms other than those which made the coal decomposed the raw material of petroleum. It may be that the chemical character of the organic material which was the base of petroleum was different from that of the coal's. There is some evidence for the latter hypothesis in the case of cannel coals. The cannel coals are free-burning and contain a great deal of oily materials. They were laid down under the same conditions as bituminous coal; but the raw material, instead of being the woody parts of plants, appeared to have been vast accumulations of wind-borne spores and pollen grains. Thus the character of the original organic material probably has something to do with the final product.

There is considerable evidence that chemical changes divorced from living organisms have also made significant contributions to petroleum formation. If plant materials, such as cotton or algae or other marine organisms, are subjected to pressures of one hundred to two hundred atmospheres at temperature of 300° C. in the presence of an alkaline material such as limestone, they produce gases such as carbon dioxide and hydrogen and an oily hydrocarbon residue.

Most of the experiments in making petroleum from carbohydrates have involved the use of a temperature of 300° C. or higher. There is good evidence that no temperatures as high as this were ever present in the beds of oil-forming materials. However, the processes might go on at the lower temperatures but at such slow rates that they could not be detected in the laboratory. Geological processes have time as an ally, for a million years in geology is an almost negligible interval. Hence, the necessity for high temperatures in the laboratory is no disproof of the low-temperature geochemical process of petroleum formation.

Whatever the process or combination of processes which entered into the making of petroleum, it is quite evident that the oily mass, after it was formed, migrated through the underground sand and silt to immense common reservoirs. The oil wells of today are merely the pockets in the earth's crust which happened to be most favorable physically for the accumulation of the oil and gas. Usually the reservoir of oil lies on top of dense rocky formations, in porous beds of sand. Gas is pocketed above the oil and water below it.

The organic residues of the past ages are not confined to coal and petroleum. Almost every large country in the world has more or less extensive deposits of sedimentary rock materials containing organic matter which will yield a satisfactory liquid fuel when subjected to destructive distillation. To these materials is given the name "oil shale," a generic term covering materials of various origins and compositions ranging from unusually dirty limestones, such as underlie the area around Chicago, Illinois, to low-grade coals. Oil shale apparently has had about the same geological history as coal—with a few details changed. The organic material is largely of plant origin. The plants grew, died, lay down, and started to decay in the conventional manner; but before decomposition by oxidation was complete they became imbedded with silt of various kinds and were buried under water or still more silt. The oxidation was halted and chemical reaction proceeded slowly along other lines, with the result that the organic matter was converted into hydrocarbons or something that gives oily hydrocarbons when heated. Even less is known about shale oil than about petroleum. The chemists have a name for it—kerogen—but that means nothing. Suffice it to say that the chemical make-up of the carboniferous constituents of oil shale is more closely related to coal than it is to liquid petroleum; but when heated the organic matter may be almost completely converted into liquid fuels. . . .

Nature's operations in laying down the world's mineral deposits have been proceeding over a span of probably two billion years. Now comes man digging into the storehouse. In one century of really active exploitation he has dug well down toward the bottom of some of the mineral bins to the two-billion-year-old storehouse. . . .

TIME UNITS			DISTINCTIVE FEATURES	OROGENY	DATES
CENOZOIC ERA	CENOZOIC PERIOD	Recent epoch		Cascadian Rev.	1 000 000
		Pleistocene epoch	The Stone Age of human history. Glaciation widespread, mountains attain present heights.		
		Pliocene epoch	Climate becomes cooler and drier. Man diverges from the apes.		
		Miocene epoch	Mammals reach climax; grazing types evolve as prairies spread. Elephants reach America.		
		Oligocene epoch	Mammals evolve rapidly. Great Apes arise in Eurasia.		
		Eocene epoch	Modern orders of mammals appear and evolve rapidly.		
		Paleocene epoch	Archaic mammals dominate. Valley glaciers appear locally.		
MESOZOIC ERA	CRETACEOUS PERIOD		Dinosaurs, pterodactyls, toothed birds reach climax and then die out. Small archaic mammals appear. Flowering plants and hard-wood forests spread widely.	Laramide Rev.	60 000 000 To 70 000 000
	JURASSIC PERIOD		Dinosaurs and marine reptiles dominate. Toothed birds appear. Ammonites reach climax.	Nevadian Dist.	
	TRIASSIC PERIOD		Small dinosaurs and the first mammals appear. Conifers and cycads dominate the forests. Ammonites evolve rapidly.	Palisade Dist.	
PALEOZOIC ERA	PERMIAN PERIOD		Continental uplift and orogeny widespread. Extremes of cold and aridity result in rapid evolution and many extinctions.	Appalachian Rev.	200 000 000
	PENNSYLVANIAN PERIOD	Carboniferous	Warm humid climate favors coal making. Reptiles and insects appear. Sporebearing trees dominate swamp forests.		
	MISSISSIPPIAN PERIOD		Shell-crushing sharks, crinoids, and lazy bryozoans attain climax.		
	DEVONIAN PERIOD		Lung-fishes evolve into air-breathing vertebrates (amphibians). First forests appear. Brachiopods reach climax.	Acadian Dist.	290 000 000
	SILURIAN PERIOD		Climate warm, locally arid. Corals form widespread reefs. First meager evidence of land life recorded.		
	ORDOVICIAN PERIOD		Seas spread widely over low continents. Many groups of inverte-brates make first appearance. Trilobites reach greatest differen-tiation.	Taconian Dist.	350 000 000
	CAMBRIAN PERIOD		Fossils abundant for the first time representing marine life only. Trilobites and brachiopods dominate. Plants recorded only as a lime-secreting algae.		400 000 000
CRYPTOZOIC EON	KEWEENAWAN PERIOD		Vast lava flows and thick red sediments cover the Lake Superior region. A geosyncline occupies the Rocky Mountain area.	Killarney Rev.	1 050 000 000
	HURONIAN PERIOD		A geosyncline occupies the Great Lakes region. Glaciation is wide-spread in Canada. Lake Superior iron ores are deposited.		
	TIMISKAMIAN PERIOD		A long period of accumulation of sedimentary rocks is followed by great disturbances and then by profound erosion of the Canadian Shield.	Algoman Rev.	
	KEEWATIN PERIOD		Thick lava flows occupy the Lake Superior region, interfingering with oldest known sedimentary rocks.	Laurentian Rev.	

PART FOUR

Earth History

In the introduction to the first section, several guesses about the age of the earth, founded on religious mythology, were mentioned. Until comparatively recently, when Hutton founded the science of geology, there existed no basis for a guess based on more logical premises. Hutton realized that the time needed to accomplish the results he observed was so great that he wrote, "I see no vestige of a beginning, no prospect of an end." In one respect, contemporary scientists are not so inconclusive. They believe they have evidence which dates the beginning of the earth, even though they remain in doubt about how the beginning occurred.

Professor Holmes, whose whole life has been spent on the subject, tells in "The Age of the Earth" how various geological clocks have been devised and what they seem to show about the time span of earth history. The rate of deposition of sedimentary strata, the salinity of the ocean and the supposed rate of consolidation and cooling of the globe have been used as measuring rods. The first method has serious limitations; the last two have such notable flaws that they have been abandoned. However, another more accurate clock, the rate of decay of the radioactive elements, has now been put to use. In the words of Professor Holmes, it is the only known process "that has operated throughout geological time and has produced measurable results at a known rate, of which the law of variation with time is also known." The portion of his article quoted in this volume ends with the sentence, "The age of the earth is . . . somewhere between three thousand and five thousand, four hundred million years." The complete article continues with a mathematical analysis incomprehensible to the lay reader, which further narrows the possibilities. At the end of the article, Professor Holmes "favors the hope that the estimate of three thousand, three hundred fifty million years for the age of the earth is unlikely to be seriously wrong." Very recent estimates, based on the recession of the galaxies and on age determinations through measurements of the speed of radioactive reactions, suggest an age of five billion years.

The history of these billions of years is known technically as "historical geology," in contradistinction to "physical geology," with which the previous sections of this book were largely concerned. The subject is introduced by a geological table, which lists the great eras, periods and epochs and by "The Record of Living Things" by Professor Hotchkiss. It concerns itself primarily with the origin and development of living things, both plants and animals. The Hotchkiss article shows how, by painstaking examination of the remains of such plants and animals, as well as of the sedimentary rocks in which they are usually found, scientists have been able to re-create the environments and life forms of pre-history. Inherent in the story is the doctrine of evolution—the appearance of low forms of life in the pre-Cambrian; the development from mysterious beginnings of the first animals with backbones, the fishes; the appearance of amphibians and of true land animals; the gradual growth of higher types known as mammals; and the culmination of the line in *Homo sapiens,* who rules the world today but who may perhaps give way to a still higher form.

The remains referred to above are known as fossils and those who study them are known as paleontologists. Percy Raymond, late Professor of Paleontology at Harvard, introduces the subject to us in "Fossils and Fossil Hunting," in which he describes the various ways in which fossils are formed and classified, how field workers go about finding them, and how they are preserved for study and exhibition.

The search for fossils is fascinating. They may be found in the nets of fishermen off the coast of South Africa or in the sandstones and conglomerates of Java. On occasion, a single great find has changed our whole conception of the growth of a species. The articles following "Fossils and Fossil Hunting" describe three highly significant developments. In "A Living Fossil" Professor J. L. B. Smith of Rhodes University College, Grahamstown, South Africa, tells about the discovery of a "very remarkable fish," supposed to have been extinct for fifty million years. This fish, the Coelacanthid, is a member of the family from which the amphibia and man are presumed to have sprung and is "a confirmatory link in the chain of evidence upon which the theory of evolution is based." Professor Smith says in his paper, published in 1939, "We hope that the advent of the other specimens will be not long delayed." Actually it was not until 1953 that another fish of the same species, in considerably better condition, was captured. During the intervening fourteen years the author walked for thousands of miles along the eastern seashore of Africa and distributed thousands of leaflets among the natives, explaining what he was looking for. A report in *The New York Times* says of the discovery of the fish, "This is much as though living dinosaurs were ambling down out of the Catskill Mountains and presenting themselves for inspection by modern physiologists."

Dr. J. C. Merriam, the noted paleontologist and late President of the Carnegie Institution of Washington, describes in "Pools That Reflect the Past" our second dramatic happening—the discovery of the asphalt lake at Rancho La Brea in California, where mastodons, saber-tooth tigers and birds larger than condors were trapped and preserved.

For over half a century, scientists have delved in the far corners of the earth to complete the jigsaw puzzle of man's most recent ancestry. In "Search for Early Man" by G. H. R. von Koenigswald, Paleontologist of the Geological Survey, Bandung, Java, we learn about the discovery of *Pithecanthropus erectus,* and of other specimens which seem to indicate that man's ancestors were giants.

The final article is "The Future of Man as an Inhabitant of the Earth" by Kirtley F. Mather, Professor of Geology at Harvard. An examination of the evidence, says Professor Mather, appears to show that the earth will be a habitable globe, capable of supplying the wants of man for thousands and perhaps hundreds of thousands of years. The problem is not one of the availability of the supply but of our use of it. Are men capable of the intelligence and good will to act with sufficient co-ordination and co-operation? Only mankind can destroy the human race. Man's future lies in his own hands. In the last analysis, it is a spiritual rather than a scientific problem.

The Age of the Earth

By Arthur Holmes

Long before it became a scientific aspiration to estimate the age of the earth, many elaborate systems of world chronology had been devised by the sages of antiquity. The most remarkable of these occult time scales is that of the ancient Hindus, whose astonishing concept of the earth's duration has been traced back to the Manusmitri, a sacred book that was probably completed in its present form about 150-120 B.C. According to this venerable compilation of law and wisdom, the whole past and future of the world is but a "day" in the eternal life of Brahma—a day of four thousand, three hundred twenty million years, throughout which finite things are being created out of the infinite. The Day of Brahma is divided into fourteen great cycles, each lasting 308,448,000 years, together with a final "twilight" period of 1,728,000 years, at the close of which, when Brahma's night begins, the finite is destined once more to merge into the infinite. At present the world is in the seventh of these cycles and, according to the Hindu calendar recorded in the Vishnu Purana, it is now (A.D. 1947) 1,972,949,048 years since the earth came into existence. By a curious coincidence this characteristically precise assessment is of the same order as the two thousand million years which has recently been the most widely favored estimate for the age of the expanding universe.

If geological concepts had developed in a community endowed in advance with so generous a concept of the past, much confusion and bitter controversy might have been avoided. But in western Europe the age of the earth had long been identified—to within a few days—with the few thousand years of mankind's history recorded in the narratives of the Old Testament. According to the interpretation of Archbishop Ussher (1581–1656) the creation of the world took place in the year 4004 B.C., and pioneer geologists whose observations suggested that the Mosaic traditions might not be scientifically reliable were branded as dangerous heretics.

A mild though significant instance of the prejudicial influence of this cramping limitation of time is afforded by a remark made by the celebrated astronomer Edmund Halley (1656–1742), in the course of a communication to the Royal Society of a "Proposal . . . to Discover the Age of the World" (1715). Halley realized that the sea had become salt because of the accumulation of saline material contributed by inflowing rivers, and he suggested that the total amount of salt in the sea might therefore provide a measure of the age of the oceans. At that time the necessary data for making the calculation were not available, and Halley lamented that the ancient Greek and Latin authors had not "delivered down to us the degree of the saltness of the sea, as it was about two thousand years ago; for then," he continued, "it cannot be doubted but that the difference between what is now found and what was then, would become very sensible." Now obviously, if Halley had been thinking in millions of years instead of thousands, he must have realized that the increase of salinity since Roman times would be quite undetectable. Nevertheless, he did not fail to slip in his suspicion that "the world may be found much older than many have hitherto imagined."

It was James Hutton (1726–1797) who first clearly grasped the full significance and immensity of geological time. In his famous "Theory of the Earth," communicated to the Royal Society of Edinburgh in 1785, he presented an irrefutable body of evidence to prove that the hills and mountains of the present day, so far from being everlasting, have themselves been carved and are still being modified by slow but inexorable processes of erosion such as those now in operation; and that the sand and mud continually removed by rivers are being slowly deposited on the sea floor as sedimentary rocks in the making. Realizing that "the past history of our globe must be explained by what can be seen to be happening now," and observing that the sedimentary strata of the earth's crust bear all the hallmarks of having accumulated exactly like those now being deposited, he saw that the vast thicknesses of these older strata implied the operation of erosion and sedimentation throughout a period that could only be described as inconceivably long. But Hutton went further. He recognized not only that the earth is a thermally and dynamically active planet, internally as well as externally; he was also the first to demonstrate that the internal activity is of a cyclic character. He saw that the present cycle of erosion—given only time enough—would eventually reduce the most vigorous landscape to sea level, and he deduced from the very existence of the landscapes, carved for the most part out of marine sediments, that these sediments must have been upheaved from the sea floors of former ages. . . .

Today we know that the earth's history has included a succession of at least ten . . . major cycles, each involving (1) thick accumulations of sediments and volcanic rocks in a subsiding belt of the crust; (2) intense compression of the belt, resulting in folding and crumpling, and accompanied by metamorphism of the deeper rocks and the formation of great masses of granite; and (3) general uplift of the belt and the wearing away of its exposed portions by denudation. . . .

Hutton's experience covered only a small proportion of the earth history now known to us, and he was therefore recording no more than the sober truth when he declared he could find "no vestige of a beginning." Unfortunately this conclusion was interpreted by most of Hutton's contemporaries to mean that, according to him, the earth never had a beginning, and so was never created. Thus, far from being welcomed, Hutton's discoveries were generally regarded with righteous horror as being contrary to the Scriptures, while he himself was accused of having "deposed the Almighty Creator of the Universe from His Office." But Hutton was not without a circle of loyal friends and admirers in Edinburgh; the modest fame in which he died over a century and a half ago soon developed into a world-wide appreciation of his genius.

Hutton himself, in the absence of guiding data, made no attempt to estimate the rates of geological processes. Many of his successors, however, exhilarated by their newly found freedom, became unduly reckless in their extravagant demands for time. In 1859, for example, Darwin estimated from the supposed rate of chalk erosion in Kent that the time required for the denudation of the

Weald and the recession of bordering escarpments of the North and South Downs to their present positions was probably about three hundred million years. We now know that this estimate was at least five times too long; but Jukes, commenting on it at the time, thought it quite as likely that the period required might have been a hundred times as long. Evidently thirty thousand million years was not considered absurdly excessive for a small fraction of geological time.

Kelvin, one of the great pioneers of geophysics, then entered the field with a dramatic counterblast against such facile assumptions of unlimited time. He argued that since there is a heat flow through the earth's crust, measurable in terms of the downward increase of temperature and the thermal conductivities of rocks, the earth could be regarded as a cooling globe which must have been progressively hotter in the past. Beyond the dim horizon of the oldest rocks he envisaged a "beginning" corresponding to the time when the earth was molten and newly born from the sun. In 1862 he set himself the problem of calculating the time that had elapsed since the earth's consolidation. Because of uncertainty in much of the data, he allowed wide limits to his solution, concluding that the observed temperature gradients would have been notably lower than they are if the crust had solidified more than four hundred million years ago, and notably higher if solidification had been completed less than twenty million years ago.

Kelvin's challenge initiated one of the many scientific controversies that enlivened Victorian times. Despite many protests, however, he finally narrowed his limits to twenty and forty million years (1897). Archibald Geikie pointed out in 1899 that the testimony of the rocks clearly denied Kelvin's thermodynamic inference that geological activities must have been more vigorous in the past than they are today; and that the known sequence of sedimentary strata could not have accumulated within the limits set by Kelvin's solution of the problem. . . .

Nevertheless, Kelvin's great authority compelled a sort of compromise, and at the turn of the century geologists who claimed more than one hundred million years were thought to be unduly rash. A few, indeed, reluctantly satisfied themselves with a more meager allowance of time, but the majority steadfastly refused to accept Kelvin's results as final. The real flaw in Kelvin's assumptions was disclosed shortly after the discovery of radioactivity, when Strutt (Lord Rayleigh) detected the presence of radium in common rocks from all parts of the world. With the demonstration that the crustal rocks contain radioactive elements and are therefore endowed with an unfailing source of heat, it became obvious that the earth is not living merely on its ancestral capital of internal heat, as Kelvin had confidently believed, but that it has an independent and regular source of income of its own. . . .

By this time the minds of the older geologists were no longer attuned to thinking in terms of thousands of millions of years and few of them were prepared to take advantage of the new discoveries. This reluctance was largely due to the fact that in 1898 Joly had resuscitated Halley's suggestion for determining the age of the oceans. Adopting the simple hypothesis that, on average, the annual amount of dissolved sodium removed by rivers from the land has remained constant throughout geological time, he found that about eighty to ninety million years would be required to furnish the total amount of sodium now present in the oceans. . . .

It is therefore of some importance to consider the present status of the sodium method. It appears from recent discussion of the relevant geochemical statistics that practically all the "chloridized" sodium in river water represents oceanic salt, either blown inland and washed down by rain, or derived from saline deposits or the pore spaces of sediments. Allowing for such "second-hand" salt, the present annual addition of new sodium is about 6×10^7 tons. Even this figure may be misleadingly high because, as Lane has pointed out, analyses are rarely made of the water from rivers when they are in flood, *i.e.*, when the content of dissolved material is at its minimum. The total accumulation of marine sodium in ocean water and sediments is estimated at about 15×10^{15} tons, less the amount initially present, which may or may not be negligible. Thus, on the assumption of past uniformity, all we can conclude is that the apparent age of the oceans is something of the order of 250 million years. But past uniformity can by no means be assumed. Present rates of weathering and erosion are far too abnormally high to be representative of the geological past. Mountain ranges and land areas in general are now much more elevated and extensive than has usually been the case. Rivers and ground waters are therefore unusually active, and, moreover, many of them drain regions that are thickly strewn with easily weathered glacial deposits. Finally, human activities of all kinds—agricultural, engineering and chemical—have still further speeded up the rates of weathering and erosion over widespread areas.

Only a crude attempt can be made to assess the effects of these considerations on the "apparent" age of the oceans. . . . Obviously the hourglass of sodium accumulation is a hopelessly variable timekeeper. The most that can be said is that its present reading is not inconsistent with an oceanic age of a few thousands of millions of years.

What we need for the accurate measurement of such immense periods is a natural process that has operated throughout geological time and has produced measurable results at a known rate, of which the law of variation with time is also known. The decay of the radioactive elements is the only known process that fulfills these stringent conditions. The radioactive methods depend on the transformation of uranium and thorium into helium and lead, and on the accumulation of these stable end products in minerals and rocks that contain the parental elements. Helium, being a gas, is liable to escape, but the lead is much more likely to be retained and so to serve as an index of age. Provided a radioactive mineral such as pitchblende or uraninite has remained unaltered by weathering or other changes, then the amount of radiogenic lead now found within it is a function of (a) the amounts of uranium and/or thorium now present and (b) of the time elapsed since the mineral first crystallized. Fortunately it is possible to discriminate between the radiogenic lead and any ordinary lead that may have been present as an initial impurity in the mineral. The parental uranium contains two chemically inseparable isotopes, UI (or U^{238}) and AcU or (or U^{235}), in atomic proportions having the present value: AcU/UI

$=1/139$. Since AcU decays much more rapidly than UI, this ratio was progressively higher in the past. The material results of the atomic transformations can be summarized as follows:

$$U^{238} \rightarrow Pb^{206} + 8 \text{ He}$$
$$U^{235} \rightarrow Pb^{207} + 7 \text{ He}$$
$$Th^{232} \rightarrow Pb^{208} + 6 \text{ He}$$

It will be noticed that in each case a specific isotope of lead is generated. Ordinary lead is a mixture of the same three isotopes, together with a fourth, Pb^{204}, which is not known to be an end product of radioactive decay. Thus, if the lead separated from the radioactive mineral is isotopically analyzed (*e.g.*, by means of the mass spectrograph) and found to contain Ph^{204}, the proportion of the latter provides an index of the amount of ordinary lead that was initially present.

The present rates of production of radiogenic lead are known with a remarkable degree of accuracy, but the question naturally arises, can we be reasonably sure that these rates have remained constant throughout geological time? apart, of course, from the inevitable slowing down due to the wearing out of the parents. In other words, can we be sure that the physical constants concerned have not varied with time? Fortunately, pleochroic haloes provide us with an unambiguous affirmative. Certain granites contain flakes of brown mica which, under the microscope, can be seen to be sprinkled with dark circular spots. These are known as pleochroic haloes and some of them, when highly magnified, reveal a beautifully developed pattern of concentric rings. A minute radioactive crystal lies at the center of each halo and the darkening of the surrounding mica is produced by the helium ions (α-particles) that are shot out in all directions. The radius of each ring corresponds to the range of the α-particles from one particular radioactive element. Careful measurements by Professor G. H. Henderson show that the rings in Pre-Cambrian haloes over one thousand million years old are just as sharply defined as those in younger rocks, and that the corresponding radii and ranges are identical. Since the range, in turn, depends on the rate of disintegration of the radioactive element concerned, it follows that the radioactive constants have not varied appreciably for at least one thousand million years.

At any given time the rate of production of a particular lead isotope depends only on the disintegration constant and amount of the parental element then present. Thus the age of a mineral, t_m, can be readily calculated from each of the three ratios Pb^{206}/U, Pb^{207}/U and Pb^{208}/Th, where these symbols here represent the percentages of the parent elements and of the isotopes of radiogenic lead now present in the mineral under investigation. . . .

A fourth value for t_m can be found from the ratio Pb^{207}/Pb^{206}.

If a mineral has remained unaltered, then all four values for t_m should be in close agreement. In practice this rarely happens, because even in the freshest-looking mineral migrations of the critical elements are likely to have occurred. Fortunately, even if the three values for t_m based on Pb^{206}/U, Pb^{207}/U and Pb^{207}/Pb^{206} are widely different, the relations between them provide criteria for assessing the true age. If there has been leakage of radon (the gaseous member of the U^{238} family), then the mineral is necessarily deficient in Pb^{206}, in this case the most probable age is given by Pb^{207}/U. If there has been loss of Pb or U or both, or gain of either or both, then the true age, or a close approximation to it (if the loss or gain occurred long ago), is given by Pb^{207}/Pb^{206}.

Although a great many radioactive minerals have been chemically analyzed, relatively few isotopic analyses of the lead have been made as yet. Professor A. O. Nier, following up Aston's pioneer work, has been the most active and successful worker in this field. As an example of a fully investigated mineral, samarskite from Spinelli Quarry, Portland, Connecticut, may be taken. The mineral occurs in a pegmatite the geological age of which is not far from the end of the Devonian Period. Here the agreement is unusually good and it can be concluded that about two hundred fifty-five million years have elapsed since the close of the Devonian Period.

In the following table some of the better established dates are listed:

Mineral	Locality	Geological Age	Probable age (millions of years)
Pitchblende	Colorado	Beginning of Tertiary	58
Pitchblende	Bohemia	Late Carboniferous	215
Samarskite	Connecticut	End of Devonian	255
Cyrtolite	New York	End of Ordovician	350
Kolm	Sweden	Upper Cambrian	440
Uraninite	Morogoro, Tanganyika	Pre-Cambrian	615
Pitchblende	Katanga, Belgian Congo	Pre-Cambrian	630
Uraninite	Rajputana, India	Pre-Cambrian	755
Uraninite	Gaya, India	Pre-Cambrian	955
Uraninite	Gordonia, S. Africa	Pre-Cambrian	1025
Uraninite	Wilberforce, Ontario	Pre-Cambrian	1035
Cleveite	Aust Agder, S. Norway	Pre-Cambrian	1090
Pitchblende	Great Bear Lake, Canada	Pre-Cambrian	1400
Davidite	Radium Hill, Australia	Pre-Cambrian	1540
Pitchblende	Martin Lake, Athabasca	Pre-Cambrian	1650
Pitchblende	Rex, Great Slave Lake	Pre-Cambrian	1850
Monazite	Bangalore, India	Pre-Cambrian	2300
Uraninite	Manitoba	Pre-Cambrian	2475
Monazite	Manitoba	Pre-Cambrian	2590
Monazite	S. Rhodesia	Pre-Cambrian	2650

The monazite from Southern Rhodesia is one of the oldest minerals so far investigated, and its great age is confirmed by analyses of other radioactive minerals from the same suite of pegmatites. The latter represent the closing phase of the plutonic activity of an Archaean orogenic cycle which is the latest of three such cycles recognized in the gold belts of Southern Rhodesia. It therefore seems highly probable that the oldest rocks of this part of Africa may date back at least three thousand million years. Since the earth must be older still, this figure can be regarded as a conservative minimum for its age.

To find a maximum for the age of the earth we may assume that when the earth began it was free from the lead isotope Pb^{207}, and that all the Pb^{207} now present in the common granitic rocks of the continental crust has since been generated from U^{235}; the time required for the generation of all the Pb^{207} is then found to be five thousand, four hundred million years. The age of the earth is therefore somewhere between three thousand and five thousand, four hundred million years.

The Record of Living Things

By W. O. Hotchkiss

In the story of the discoveries of the Scotch farmer, Hutton, it was indicated briefly that successive beds of sand, lime mud and clay had been deposited over large areas. In the story of the Wisconsin millpond mention was made that some of the layers were found to contain the remains of leaves which had settled in the pond with the mud. During the deposition of the sands and clays and lime mud, which were hardened into rock to make the cliffs that Hutton examined, there were likewise deposited the remains of various living things—shells, skeletons of animals, pieces of vegetation, all sorts of things that might leave their imprints when these unconsolidated materials were later hardened into rocks. Such remains of living things have been of great value in helping us to unravel the story of the past from the study of these various rock beds.

As men studied these remains more and more, they noted that individual beds were characterized by certain types of animal and vegetable forms. Other beds above or below were characterized by different types. About one hundred years ago it began to be recognized that these remains, which are called fossils, are so definitely characteristic of the beds in which they occur that they make a most excellent means of identifying particular beds wherever they are found. When a certain group of fossils was found in a bed in eastern New York and the same group of fossils in the same kind of bed could be traced clear across the country from quarry to quarry, from hillside to hillside, it became apparent that this particular bed must have been deposited in a sea of that extent and that conditions in this sea were favorable to the existence of this kind of shells.

As lower, and therefore older, beds were examined it was found that in a general way the living forms were simpler as the age of the beds increased. As the overlying beds were examined, it was found that the forms of life usually became more complex, until in the more recent of these beds remains of higher animals and of man were found. As a result of these studies it was found that the whole series of beds laid down in the past could be divided into groups characterized by the forms of life which they contained. On the basis of this life history of the past the geologic eras have been named.

The oldest rocks found are those of the Proterozoic Era. They contain either no evidence of life or evidence that is very hazy and indefinite. Such fossils as exist are chiefly of microscopic simple forms, single-celled animals and plants like those we find in the waters of the sea and lakes today. Few of these earliest forms of life possessed hard parts that could be readily preserved.

After long ages, toward the end of the Proterozoic Era, and at the beginning of the next era, some living forms began to protect themselves with a hard shell or "exterior skeleton." Still later on larger and more complex organisms appeared, various kinds of shellfish and other small forms of life, much like those we find along our seacoasts and lake beaches today. About the middle of this era the first fishes began to appear, the earliest animals to possess a backbone. Toward the close of the era some of these developed the capacity to breathe and so to live on land as well as in water and thus became the first of what we call amphibians. This period of life development is given the name of the Paleozoic Era, which means "early life era."

The third great era was characterized by the development of enormous land animals and has been called the "age of Reptiles." This era has been given the name of Mesozoic, meaning "middle forms of life." The great dinosaurs, which reached their highest development at this time, were among the largest land animals ever to inhabit the face of the globe. Most of them were animals that laid eggs, just as fish and turtles and alligators do at present. Most of them left their young to hatch out and care for themselves unaided from the day they were born. Their lives were easy, and they prospered and developed many different forms. Some were plant-eating and some were fish-eating. Some of them found it easiest to get their food by swimming in the seas of those days and gradually developed the capacity to live in water. These reversed the experience of their ancestors who had developed from fish that got tired of living in the water and developed lungs so that they could live on the land.

Toward the end of the Mesozoic Era a higher type of animal appeared which brought forth its young alive and cared for them and nursed them through a period of infancy. This great group of animals rules the earth today. They are known as mammals, a term which includes all animals which nurse their young. Just as some of the reptiles of the Mesozoic Era found an easier livelihood by returning to the sea to live, so in this later era some of the mammals found it desirable to live in the water. Thus were developed the whales, dolphins and porpoises, inhabitants of our seas today, which bear living young and nurse them. This latest era of geologic time, which followed the Age of Reptiles, or Mesozoic Era, is given the name of the Age of Mammals, or Cenozoic Era. . . .

You will notice . . . that the grand divisions of geologic time are known as "eras." These are divided into "periods" which are in turn subdivided into "epochs." Epochs are further subdivided into "ages," but that is getting too far into technical detail. The division of the geologic past into epochs and ages has been by no means fully worked out. Much remains to be done before our knowledge is complete. Further study will lead geologists to amend the geologic table as new facts are discovered. Geology, like all other sciences, is a progressing, developing state of knowledge, no field of which will be completely known for long ages.

Each of the divisions of geologic time is, on a much grander scale, similar to the "epoch" of the deposits in the Wisconsin millpond. As that began with the building of a dam which changed the conditions from those of an eroding valley to those of quiet water where the stream deposited its sediment, so each of them began with some event that changed the previous conditions. Nothing so insignificant as the building of a dam marked these eras, but some vaster thing, such as the slow submergence by the sea of half a continent, or the elevation of a great chain of mountains. The most important changes marked the close of one era and the beginning of another. Less important changes of this kind marked the ends of periods, epochs and ages.

The close of the Paleozoic Era (early life) was marked by a great earth movement, estimated to have occurred about one hundred and eighty million years ago. This movement compressed and tilted the rocks that now make the Appalachian Mountains and raised them and the whole eastern part of the United States above sea level. How long a time this took we do not know, but we do know enough to feel quite sure that the process was too slow to be noticed by any casual observer, had there been one present. At the rate of one inch per year the highest peak in the Appalachians could have been elevated from sea level in seventy-five thousand years. In some parts of our country there are probably vertical movements of the earth's surface now going on at this rate, or even more rapid rates, which are entirely unnoticed by the people living there. Yet it is probable that the building of the Appalachian Mountains took place at a slower rate and occupied a much longer time.

The close of the Paleozoic and the beginning of the Mesozoic Eras, then, were marked by the mountain-building uplift that resulted in our Appalachian ranges. The end of the Mesozoic and the beginning of the Cenozoic Eras were similarly marked by the elevation and folding of the Rocky Mountains. . . . This was approximately sixty million years ago. Our Rocky Mountains apparently are mere youths, only a third as old as their feeble grandfathers in the East.

The Sierra and Coast ranges along our west coast are mere infants, only about a third as old as the Rockies or perhaps even less.

The events marking the ends of geologic eras have been mentioned because of their bearing on the story of living things shown by the rocks. The elevation of vast areas above sea level, or depression below it, changed living conditions very greatly. Ocean currents were deflected into new courses. Where there had been warm water there was perhaps now cold, and vice versa. Organisms that had thrived before died under the changed conditions or underwent modifications that adapted them to the change. New types of organisms immigrated and ate up or drove out the old. So there were vast changes in the kinds of remains of life that were deposited in the sediments of the sea and shore. If you will consult a textbook of geology and will turn first to the illustrations of the fossils found in Paleozoic rocks and then to those found in Mesozoic, you will find that even without knowing anything about their long specific names or attempting to qualify yourself as a paleontologist (one who studies fossils) you can see quite notable differences.

. . . There are a number of epochs in each era and the average length of each of these epochs for the last two hundred and ninety-nine million years is more than twenty million years. In one of the epochs there was time for many changes in living forms to take place. When we consider the wide variety of kinds and sizes of dogs and cattle produced in a relatively few centuries by careful breeding, and then try to think of what might happen in only one geologic epoch of an average length of twenty million years, and then, if imagination is not already stretched to the breaking point, try to still further multiply this by fifty to get the record of a billion years, it is not difficult to see how living things in their struggles for existence have had ample time to develop from the simplest forms of one-celled beings to that exceedingly complex, little understood, but "inordinately proud" being that calls himself man.

One of the great steps toward dominating the earth was the development of life forms that were able to live upon and occupy the land. All the earlier forms were probably water dwellers. In earliest times the land was barren of plants and animals. No living thing grew or crawled beyond the shore. If by accident it was left out of water, it promptly died. There is evidence that this condition prevailed in all the history of the earth up to a half-billion years ago. The landscape then consisted of bare rocks and sand and mud, deposits lying stark and naked as the rains and rivers of those ages left them. The landscape must have looked like a desert; yet in most of the world the rainfall was about as abundant as it is today.

Remains found in the rocks indicate that about five hundred million years ago, in the Cambrian Period, some few of the plants—which previously had all been sea plants

—had found a way to live on land. They were the highest plant forms of their time, even though they were only algae and the simplest of mosses. They first found a precarious living along the rocks of the seacoast. Later on, after a hundred million years of progressive adjustment to their "new" surroundings, they began to look somewhat like some of the plants we see today.

About three hundred million years ago plants had developed swamp-living forms of moderate size, and in the Carboniferous Period, two hundred and fifty million years ago, great tree ferns and similar forms grew to a height of eighty feet. These forms and their associates accumulated in their swamp homes to considerable thickness, so that today they make one of our most valuable mineral resources. They used the sunlight of those days to transform water and carbon dioxide from the air into woody cellulose which was altered into the coal which we now use to drive our trains, run our factories and light our homes. In fact, we might truly say that our present civilization is largely based on the sunshine that fell on the earth two hundred and fifty million years ago.

Plants continued to develop newer and better and more complex forms. About two hundred million years ago, in the Permian Epoch, the first cone-bearing trees appeared. About one hundred million years ago, in the Cretaceous Period, seed-bearing plants developed in abundance. Most plants up to that time had been spore bearers like our ferns today. When the first seed bearers appeared, they were so much better fitted to land conditions that they quickly became the dominant type of vegetation, a position which they hold today. They include all our grasses and grains and our fruit- and nut-bearing trees. The spore bearers have literally been relegated to the shade by the seed bearers.

It is a most interesting thing to study this development of plant life as portrayed in the rocks. We see the evident striving for adjustment to prevailing living conditions. We see the plants making experiments, as it were, trying to see whether this kind of change or that would permit them to conquer and occupy territory from which they had hitherto been debarred. We find that some experiments were huge successes, the plants quickly multiplying to cover large areas. If the experiment was not a success or developed a form adapted only to a temporary set of living conditions, the plants soon died out and disappeared from the earth. Thus all through the record in the rocks we can read of gradual improvement and progress toward a perfection still to be attained. It is as though the Creator had implanted a yearning for perfection in the first living things and we were privileged to sit and watch this progress from the crudest beginnings to the present through the whole long procession of a billion years.

The development of animal life has a similar history. The earliest animal forms are concealed in the hazy and indistinct records of the very ancient—rocks. At first all animals, like plants, were sea dwellers and were long in developing hard parts, such as shells or bones, that would not be easily destroyed and "sunk without trace."

In rocks of the Cambrian Period, which began more than five hundred million years ago, we find our first well-preserved evidence of an abundance of animal life. In older rocks, fossils are few in numbers not because living beings were scarce but because few of them had discovered how to utilize the lime in the water to build themselves stony protective armor. When this discovery was made, the rocks at once began to preserve the remains of an abundance of different forms of life, many of them quite complex in their organization. Those who have studied the long, slow evolution of living forms from the lowest to the highest have estimated that from 60 to 90 per cent of this evolution occurred before the Cambrian Period began. We find in these Cambrian rocks the remains of many hundreds of species of animals. Some are shellfish somewhat like our modern clams and oysters, others are similar to modern snails in having coiled shells, and still others are like corals in structure.

The largest and most complex animal of those times was a trilobite about twenty inches long. It possessed most of the organs found in the animals of the present day. It had a well-developed digestive tract, feeling organs, a co-ordinated muscular system, an external protective shell like the crab and lobster of today, eyes, and a well-developed nervous system with a central brain of minute size. It had all our five senses with the possible exception of hearing and smelling.

The next step in the evolution of animal life, the conquest of the land, required what to us seems a long period of time—perhaps one hundred and fifty million years. It could not be completed until plants had become land dwellers. The earliest land animals found in the rocks are insects, spiders and scorpions, which appeared about three hundred and sixty million years ago in the Silurian Period, and reached a high development in the Mesozoic Era, which covered the period of time from one hundred and eighty million to one hundred million years ago.

The first vertebrate skeleton was owned by an ancestral fish that lived perhaps four hundred million years ago in the Ordovician Period. He had found that he needed something to keep his head from being driven back into his body as he swam about in search of his prey, and so he grew a bony skeleton and discovered that life was easier. His predecessors all had "external skeletons," or shells, that were good armor against his enemies but were cumbersome and cut down the speed with which they could navigate and catch the other organisms upon which they lived. This development of a backbone was an improvement of such great usefulness that all higher types of animals since that time have an internal jointed skeleton, the main feature of which is a flexible, jointed backbone. Nothing has been invented by Nature thus far that is better for its purpose than this great device. It has been the prime factor that has enabled animals to attain to great size.

Since the first animal with a vertebrate skeleton appeared four hundred million years ago, there has been progress in size, until today we now have the largest animal that ever lived, the great blue whale, which is known to have attained a length of one hundred and six feet. Progress was not rapid. One hundred million years had to pass after the invention of the backbone before animals ten feet long developed. It was not until the vertebrates took to living on the land that development to great size occurred. In the Age of Reptiles—the Mesozoic Era—when the dinosaurs and their kin were lords of creation, they so "quickly" added to their size that no more than thirty or forty million years of this era elapsed before they had attained to maximum lengths of seventy feet. This experiment of increasing the bulk of flesh inside one skin—or, to look at it from the inside out, the bulk of flesh surrounding a single backbone—was successful for about seventy-five million years, and the great animals of the period prospered for a time lasting from one hundred and fifty million years ago to seventy-five million years ago.

The development of these animals to greater size was not accompanied by corresponding brain development. The largest brain of those days was less than a quarter the size of yours or mine. . . .

In the meantime Nature was making a different kind of experiment. The great reptiles did not have any marked maternal instincts. Most of them continued the practice which characterized the poor fish and lower animals that had been left behind in the race. They laid eggs and left their young to hatch out and care for themselves. About one hundred and fifty million years ago there appeared some small animals that hatched their eggs inside their bodies and produced living young, which they nursed and cared for through a period of helpless infancy. From this habit of nursing their young they have been given the name of mammals. With them the great quality of mother love first began to be an important factor in the life of the earth. Through at least eight hundred and fifty million long years of the billion-year story living beings got along with little or none of the mother love that is so powerful an influence in the lives of all of the higher animals today.

Mammals also gave up an old practice followed by all other living things, that of being cold-blooded. They found that to elevate the blood temperature gave them advantages over their cold-blooded associates. Warm blood and the habit of nursing their young were the most important new elements in life that distinguished the mammals. They had the same organs, muscles, nervous system and brain as their cold-blooded, egg-laying neighbors, but they had in the two new improvements qualities that were to make them, after a hundred millions of years had elapsed, the dominant type of animals on the face of the globe. For the last sixty million years they have prospered more extensively than any other kind of animal life.

The story told by the rocks relates that, after the success

of the mammals as a dominant type of animal life, Nature began another major experiment, the development of a larger brain. The invention of the shell or external skeleton she had bettered by inventing the jointed backbone. This had made possible the reptilian conquest of the land. The reptilian experiment she had largely discarded after the successful development of mammals.

Before this last experiment the largest brain in the world was probably no larger than one-quarter the size of the average human brain, was much less finely organized, and was much less than a quarter as capable.

In early Tertiary time, during the first period of the ascendancy of mammals, there was one kind that began to live in trees. In all animals living on the ground the sense of smell had been highly developed and was most useful. In the tree dwellers this sense lost its importance, and the sense of sight became of greater value. Consequently, sight was developed more highly as the ages rolled on. The conformation of the skull changed so that the two eyes could look straight ahead and both eyes could see the same object. This change was associated with a corresponding development of the parts of the brain which related to vision. This made possible the kind of vision that enables its possessor to estimate distances. If a ground dweller does not estimate distance correctly when leaping for his prey, he only loses a meal. If a tree dweller misjudges the distance of a branch he leaps for, he is in a far worse plight —he is quite likely to lose his life. The quickness of movement of these tree dwellers undoubtedly made increased brain capacity a great asset to them, and so those with better brains prospered and propagated their kind.

Tree dwelling developed the grasping capacity of the extremities and the capacity to balance and walk on the hind legs. All these things made brains more of an asset. The grasping capacity of the forelimbs permitted the use of clubs, which began to come into style as weapons.

When the tailless, hind-foot-walking, manlike apes—anthropoids—appeared in the Oligocene Epoch, about forty million years ago as the story of the rocks reveals, brain capacity increased. Some of the best of these apes had brains one-third the size of man's.

The oldest erect-walking man, whose skull was found in

the rocks of Java, had a brain 60 per cent as large as ours. The rocks in which his remains were found date back possibly to a period from two to five million years ago—the late Pliocene Epoch—but the number of years is getting so short that our measuring scale is very inaccurate. Whether this time is two million or ten million we do not know. Whether this Java man is really to be classed as low-type man or a high type of anthropoid is not a matter on which all scientists agree. What is more important is that his brain was about 60 per cent as large as that of modern man.

After the time of the Java man came the great change in climate which produced the Glacial Epoch . . . when great continental ice sheets spread over the land from the north. South of the margin of the ice the climate became colder. Man had to develop to meet this emergency, or perish. He already had the capacity to use clubs, bones and stones as weapons. At this time he probably learned to use fire, to live in caves, and to build himself shelters in which he could find relief from the cold. The remains found in the rocks tell this story in a sketchy fashion which as yet is far from satisfactory, but they do inform us positively of the facts given above and also of the size of his brain cavity, which was 90 per cent as large as ours.

This brings us to the scientific domain of the anthropologist, where we may leave the development of the human brain and its tremendous significance.

To see the success of this latest experiment of Nature—the development of the brain—you need only look about you, and, with the background of the story of a billion years, consider how completely man dominates the world in which he lives, how he has mastered fire, water, earth and air, how he has tamed the lightning of the heavens and made it his servant, how he has learned to bring wealth from a depth far below the surface and use it for his convenience, how he has multiplied in numbers and learned to control all other forms of life and the great forces of Nature so that they minister to his welfare.

I once heard a friend facetiously remark that it was too bad that Moses was not a better geologist. And continuing, he said, "If he had been, instead of writing a story of the *fall of man* and his decline from previous perfection he could have written a much more inspiring and hopeful tale of the *rise of man* from lowly beginnings in the remote past, with the unlimited possibilities of the future before him." It is truly a most satisfying experience in reverence for the Creator of all things to read in the record not made by human hands this great story of the past and then to turn and look into the future which is developing so rapidly before our eyes.

Fossils and Fossil Hunting
By Percy Raymond

Much has been written in recent years about the early history of the earth in so far as it can be deduced from astronomical and physical data. The evolution of the world would have been futile, however, had it not been for the introduction of life. As to how life originated, geology unfortunately gives little information, but that the earth has supported life for countless millions of years is clearly shown by the remains of animals and plants entombed within the sedimentary rocks during their accumulation and preserved to the present time. These remains serve a twofold purpose. Not only do they give a clue to the history of life upon the globe, but, when properly studied and interpreted, they reveal much of its physical history. What prehistoric implements are to the archaeologist or the inscriptions incised by ancient peoples upon enduring rock are to the historian, such are fossils to the geologist. Fortunately, their study is not nearly so difficult as that of artifacts or inscriptions, nor does it require so technical a training; yet it produces results of the same order of accuracy.

To study fossils it is necessary to have some knowledge of living animals and plants, for fossils are either more or less perfectly preserved remains of organisms, or evidences of their former existence. At best they are less complete than recent specimens, so that, unless something is known of the modern fauna and flora, one is totally unable to interpret the fragments found in the rocks. . . .

What is the process of becoming a fossil? It is merely preservation, either by the checking of decomposition or by the replacement of the hard parts by some relatively durable substance. Anything unfavorable to the life of bacteria impedes decay. Very dry air, a low temperature, sea or bog water, burial in mud or volcanic ash, an incrustation of pitch, gum or calcium carbonate, all have a more or less preservative effect, so that decomposition is either retarded or entirely prevented. When bacteria are entirely excluded not only the hard but the soft parts as well may be preserved as in a modern refrigerating plant. The most famous instances of cold storage are those of the remains of mammoths and rhinoceroses occasionally found in the frozen gravels and ice of Siberia. Another case of remarkable preservation is that of insects in amber. While it was a sticky gum exuded from a species of pine, numerous insects were trapped in it, to be preserved as it hardened. Although amber of many ages is known, the most abundant insect-bearing material is found in the Oligocene strata on the Prussian shores of the Baltic.

Suppose an organism to be buried in some substance which retards decay. Conceivably the sand, clay or calcareous ooze which surrounds it may become sufficiently compacted while the organism retains its original form to hold its shape. Then subsequent decay of the object will leave a hollow mold. This may be preserved as such, in which case it would itself be a fossil, or percolating waters may eventually fill it with calcite, silica, pyrite, mud or even sand. . . .

There is another type of replacement in which decay of the skeleton occurs in the presence of mineralized waters, so that for each particle removed the water gives up a bit of its mineral matter, producing a delicate replica of the whole original structure. The conditions favorable to this process have, however, rarely obtained. A few localities have furnished most such specimens, a noteworthy one being a thin layer of coal in the Carboniferous of England. The so-called "coal balls" found in it are really calcareous concretions in which a part of the vegetation which formed the coal has been replaced by calcium carbonate. Those who have visited the Petrified Forest of Arizona or other areas of "badlands" in the western states have probably noticed the great amount of petrified wood which, although entirely changed to stone, still shows the characteristic rings of growth, knots and other features of modern trees. This type of preservation is much more commonly found in the replacement of plants than of animals.

Some fossils are so preserved that they retain indications of the shape of the internal organs of animals, even though no tissues actually remain. Thus there are certain creatures which commonly ingest large quantities of mud with their food. The mud-filled alimentary tracts of a few such organisms have been recovered, showing the shape of stomach and intestines. Coprolites, the fossil excrement of animals, also show something of the shape of the alimentary canal but are particularly interesting because many of them contain undigested remains of food. . . .

Skeletons which consist essentially of compounds of carbon—that is, those of plants, fish and invertebrates with chitinous coverings, such as insects, crustaceans and similar animals—are commonly preserved as a black, filmy residue, showing the form more or less perfectly but much or even entirely flattened. The change in this case seems to be a chemical one, involving the loss of the volatile constituents and reducing the composition to a state of approximating that of coal. . . .

Artificial structures made by organisms are occasionally found. Some burrowing animals lined their habitations with bits of shells or sand which they cemented together, whereas others made nests which are occasionally preserved in the rocks. The most abundant artificial structures are the various implements of prehistoric man.

To recapitulate, the states of preservation in which fossils are found may be tabulated.

Actual remains of organisms
    with the soft tissues preserved
    with only the skeleton preserved
    with the skeleton partially changed by addition of
        mineral matter
    with tissues carbonized
Natural molds of organisms

Replacements of the hard parts of organisms
    Skeleton petrified
        without loss of structural details
        with loss of structural details
    Skeleton replaced by natural casts
        mechanically, by infiltration of sand or mud into natural molds (often called external casts)
        chemically, by deposition of mineral matter in the same
    Natural casts of cavities in the hard parts (commonly called internal casts)
  Impressions of organisms
  Tracks, trails and burrows
  Artificial structures made by organisms
  Coprolites

. . . The term "fossil," which referred originally to anything dug up from the earth, has been restricted to the various classes of organic remains listed above. It is difficult to frame a brief definition which is both inclusive and exclusive, but it may be said that fossils are the remains of organisms or the direct evidences of their former existence, preserved by natural causes in the earth's crust. This definition, although generally acceptable, has the fault of being rather too inclusive, since it makes no reference to the time of burial. As a matter of convenience many paleontologists, including the author, arbitrarily exclude from the category of fossils all things which have been buried since the beginning of historic times. . . .

The task of the paleontologist is to reconstruct from such materials as he finds in sedimentary rocks the animal and vegetable life of the period during which the strata were in the process of accumulation. Too often he must rely upon incomplete, distorted and broken objects which are not easily interpreted. The solution of his difficulties can come only through comparison: first, with other materials from the same strata, in the endeavor to bring together scattered parts belonging to the same sort of animal or plant; and second, with such modern organisms as appear to be related. A wide knowledge of the comparative anatomy of modern organisms is therefore a necessary part of the equipment of the paleontologist. Fragmentary material must be pieced together to build up a whole skeleton. Then from scars of muscles, shapes of bones or shells, and such other features as may be preserved, it may be possible to arrive at a rough approximation of the form of the animal as it appeared in life. . . .

If one is to be able to speak of any particular kind of animal or plant, it must have a name; so to each kind, or species, a name is given by the person who first publishes a description of it. Many experiments were made before a definite system of nomenclature was finally reached, about the year 1758. It was natural to try not only to assist the memory by applying a descriptive name but also to indicate the relationship of the particular animal or plant to other organisms. Men naturally like to get their knowledge into as orderly, usat le and easily remembered form as possible, and so with the naming there became involved the idea of classification. It is obvious that certain modern animals are more closely related to each other than they are to others. Anyone would say at first glance that a cat and a tiger are more closely related to each other than either is to a cow. Yet the cow is more like a cat than it is like a fish. Thus the classification of plants or animals is built up about degrees of likeness or unlikeness. The name given to the particular kind is intended to furnish a knowledge of at least one degree of relationship, as well as to serve as a convenience in mentioning it. The earlier writers, who were unnecessarily descriptive, gave names a whole sentence long. Linnaeus, the great Swedish naturalist, about 1758 set the fashion now followed, of cutting the name down to two words, the first or generic name indicating relationship, and the second or specific name suggesting, ideally, some outstanding characteristic of the organisms described. It is usual to compare the generic name with the family name among people and the specific name with the Christian name. The generic name is given to a group of species which are found to be very closely related in the structure of their bones, teeth, muscles, et cetera, but each of the various kinds within a group has a specific name. Thus the genus of the cats is *Felis;* the lion is *Felis leo,* the tiger *Felis tigris,* and the house cat *Felis catus.* The generic name shows their evident close relationship, and the specific name indicates which particular kind of cat is meant. . . .

There are different ideas about the relationships of various organisms to one another; hence one should not expect to find textbooks in agreement about classification. In a general way, the species is the unit in the system, just as the inch is the unit in the widely used British system of mensuration. Although it is true that no definite number of species is required to make up a genus, the next higher unit, there is nevertheless a feeling that if a genus has a very large number of species it is capable of subdivision; hence subgeneric names may be employed to designate groups of closely related species. Genera are brought together in families; large families may be split up by the erection of groups called subfamilies. Families are gathered under orders, or, in some cases, into superfamilies under the orders. The orders are considered as subdivisions of classes or, in large classes, of subclasses. The classes are major groups under the phyla, the phylum being the largest unit ordinarily used, although the term "kingdom" is still in use for the two great divisions of organisms, animal and vegetable.

Although the species is the unit, it can be subdivided, just as the inch can be divided into a certain number of barleycorns and lines. Many systematic zoölogists recognize subspecies, and even give names to varieties, so that the Latin name may be a trinomial or even a polynomial, thus reverting to the condition which obtained before the time of Linnaeus. Fortunately, few paleontologists have got beyond the trinomial; most of us retain the binomial system. After all, a name is a purely artificial thing, employed for convenience. If the endeavor to make it descriptive, either of characteristics or relationship, causes it to become so long as to be cumbersome, it ceases to fulfill its original purpose.

A surprising number of students each year ask for an example of the use of these terms; one is therefore inserted here.

Kingdom *Animalia*. Includes all animals
  Phylum *Chordata*. All animals with a notochord
    Class *Mammalia*. Animals which suckle the young

Subclass *Eutheria*. Mammals with placenta
 Order *Primates*. Mammals with flat nails
Suborder *Anthropoidea*. Tailless, semi-erect or erect
  primates
 Family *Hominidae*. Erect, large-brained anthro-
  poids
  Genus *Homo*. Anthropoids with the modern type
   of brain
   Species *Homo sapiens*. Men with chins, "even
    as you and I"

Many an innocent youth will in later life express himself in print. He should remember that generic names
begin with a capital letter, specific names with a small
one. Both should be printed in italics.

Collecting Fossils

Where are fossils found? Many people know them only
as exhibited in museums and do not encounter them in the
ordinary routine of their lives. In my own case, I began
as a schoolboy a collection of the rocks and minerals to be
found within ten or fifteen miles of my birthplace in southwestern Connecticut and was naturally led to read such
books on geology as were in my home or in the local
library. Since these books devoted a great deal of space
to fossils, it became my highest ambition to add some of
them to my collection, and even though the books explicitly
stated that fossils did not occur in granites and gneisses,
the rocks of the surrounding country, I spent many a
fruitless day searching for them. The books did say that
they were to be found in limestone, but I hunted through
the limestone quarries north of my usual haunts with no
better success. As a result of years of such efforts I became
firmly convinced that fossils were scarce objects, an impression which I have since found to prevail not only
among those who live upon the ancient metamorphic rocks
of New England but also among those who dwell in regions
where the strata are really high fossiliferous. . . .

As a matter of fact, fossils occur almost everywhere.
There are several localities for them even among the "everlasting hills" of New England. They may be expected in any

region of unmetamorphosed sedimentary strata, and if one looks at a geological map of North America, he finds that such rocks cover a much greater area than those of igneous or metamorphic origin. . . .

Hunting for, and collecting, invertebrate fossils require no particular preparation or equipment, although the person who knows what he is looking for usually finds the best specimens, and a certain amount of skill is required if it is necessary to break them from the rocks. A paleontologist is often asked how deep one has to dig in order to find fossils. As a matter of fact, one seldom does any digging unless a particular layer is found to be so productive that it is worth while to remove other layers to get at it. If sedimentary rocks had been left by Nature in the position in which they were laid down, with the older buried beneath the younger, it would be necessary to dig deeply to obtain representatives of the more ancient faunas, but there are few strata, except those deposited in the deep oceans, which have not been subjected at some time to folding, faulting and uplift, so that rocks of all ages appear at the surface at one place or another. To find their fossils it is only necessary to visit the exposures in cliffs, along the sides of ravines, in stream beds, quarries and excavations along railroads and highways. In some cases one must break the fossils from the rocks which contain them, but the best specimens are those which through the action of frost, rain, alternations of heat and cold, or other natural causes have been freed, or as it is called, weathered, from the matrix. . . .

Although invertebrate fossils are common and fully as worthy of study as any, the ones which attract most attention are the larger and more showy bones of the vertebrates. These are seldom found or collected except by trained men who go to the regions where they are known to occur. Occasional specimens are found by people not professionally engaged in their study, but these are apt to be ruined by the zealous collector, who is always overanxious to secure his specimen and is ignorant of the methods by which it might be preserved. It is perhaps worth-while to describe briefly three of the most famous regions for vertebrate fossils, the chalk of western Kansas, the Tertiary deposits east of the Rocky Mountain region, and the dinosaur beds of the United States and Canada.

The chalk deposits of western Kansas were first explored in the years between 1870 and 1875. . . . The prize fossils of this region consist of fish ten to fifteen feet long, aquatic reptiles fifteen to fifty feet long, flying reptiles and toothed birds. Although the rock is soft, it is not possible to dig out the individual bones of the skeleton separately, for all are crushed, distorted and flattened to such an extent that, if they were separately removed, most of the thinner ones would be broken and destroyed, the larger ones hopelessly mixed up, and both so moved from their natural association as to lose much of their significance. The material must therefore be taken out in slabs. The finest specimens are those which, when found, are entirely covered by rock excepting for the tip of some extremity such as the snout, tail, fin or paddle. Since few of the skeletons are complete, when one sees a bone, or bones, projecting on an outcrop, the first thing to do is to determine what the animal is and how much of the specimen still remains. No bones are removed until the rock has been cleared from the entire surface. Then if the exploratory work shows that all or a considerable part of a skeleton is present, and not, as too often proves to be the case, merely one or two odd bones, enough of it is uncovered to learn its extent. When it has been outlined, and as much of the cover has been taken away as seems safe, a trench is dug around the specimen, the depth varying with the size of the fossil and the thickness of the layer in which it is embedded. If the animal is small, covering an area of no more than five by seven or eight feet, an attempt is made to get it out in one slab, the exposed surface having first been covered with wet paper, or cheesecloth soaked in poisoned gum arabic or glue, to make the bones firm and keep them in place. Often it is necessary to follow this coating with burlap soaked in plaster of Paris. After the upper surface has been secured against breakage, the layer in which the fossil is preserved is pried up by means of wedges, picks and bars, and tilted up with levers; a frame is built around it, the specimen is turned over, and the box is completed. Then it may be hoisted with an improvised derrick onto a wagon or truck and started for the railroad. When specimens are too large to be moved as one slab, they are cut into the requisite number of pieces, the division being made where as few bones as possible will be affected, care being taken to preserve all parts of broken bones. In some cases an almost entire skeleton has been found which has been exposed so long that it is badly weathered and seems hardly worth collecting. Such specimens have been saved by coating the upper surface with plaster and cleaning the matrix from the lower side, a process which reveals the unweathered sides of the bones, the plaster taking the place of the original rock.

The fresh-water Tertiary deposits of the high plains east of the Rockies, and of the intermontane valleys within and west of them, provide an extensive field for search in beds ranging in age from Paleocene to Pleistocene. . . .

The chief localities for remains of dinosaurs in North America are in the third region, along the flanks of the Rocky Mountains and the plains to the eastward, from Alberta to Colorado, the richest finds of Jurassic dinosaurs having been made in Colorado, Utah and Wyoming, and of Cretaceous species in eastern Wyoming, central Montana and along the Red Deer River in Alberta, Canada.

These great American reptiles are of comparatively recent discovery, the first having been brought to the attention of paleontologists and the scientific public in 1877, although hunters and travelers had seen the bones and had even brought back sections of them as pieces of petrified wood before that. In 1877 three observers, one a schoolteacher, another a professor in the School of Mines at Golden, Colorado, and the third a section foreman on the Union Pacific Railroad, found dinosaur bones. As the late Samuel W. Williston once said, their discovery was not nearly so remarkable as that the dinosaurs had remained so long unnoticed. "The beds containing them had been studied for years by the geologists of the Hayden and King surveys, yet in some areas acres were literally strewn with bones and fragments of bones, and at what has since been known as the Bone Cabin Quarry in central Wyoming, a Mexican sheep herder had built the foundations of a cabin by cording up the huge limb bones of dinosaurs." . . .

Hunting for dinosaurs is the same process as hunting for any other vertebrate fossil. The areas and formations which can be expected to yield specimens are well known, and because of the large size of the bones one would think that by this time all possible specimens must have been discovered. But anyone who has been in the "badlands" realizes how innumerable are the little dry draws or ravines that intersect the hills, how great the exposures, and above all, how rapid erosion is when it does rain. Instead of being exhausted, each year sees the dinosaur country producing new and more nearly perfect specimens, for the storehouse appears to be constantly renewing itself. . . .

A Living Fossil
(*Latimeria chalumnae*) J. L. B. Smith
By J. L. B. Smith

Scientific discovery rarely follows a smooth and orderly course. Like most natural processes it proceeds spasmodically, and important results frequently come only after long drawn-out, exhausting, and apparently fruitless endeavor, sometimes even almost by what appears to be a lucky chance. Scientific discoveries may roughly be divided into two main classes: Those which affect the material welfare of mankind (*e.g.,* the existence and action of bacteria) and those which represent merely an addition to knowledge. There has recently been discovered near East London, South Africa, a very remarkable fish which represents an event of the latter sort. The interest it has aroused is on account of the great scientific importance which attaches to it. It is a living link with a past so remote as to be almost beyond the grasp of the ordinary mind. . . .

Beyond the disputes of scientists about minor points is the fact that fishes of sorts were the ancestral forms from which all other vertebrate creatures have originated. We have no record of any accepted "link" between these fishes and their most likely invertebrate ancestors. The fishes are suddenly there, some three hundred and seventy million years ago, in numbers, and in a diversity of weird forms. From the fishes originated the amphibia, and from them the reptiles. These were all cold-blooded creatures, very much at the mercy of sudden climatic changes. The first amphibia appeared about three hundred and twenty million years ago, and reptiles evolved from them by ninety to one hundred million years later. Those sluggish creatures were produced by Nature in great diversity of size and shape, but most of the larger forms in specialized groups have become extinct.

The call for greater activity and mobility produced from the reptiles the warm-blooded birds and mammals, the latter class, as typified by man, being now dominant on the earth.

To return to those early fishes, some of which were our ancestors: Many of them, the only ones we know, left traces in the rocks. Usually the skeleton and any teeth, spines or hard skins are preserved, in rare cases perfectly. The "soft parts" are largely unknown, and the reconstructed outlines of extinct forms are to some extent guesswork, but no more guesswork than the diagnosis of appendicitis by a physician. In each case visualization of the hidden condition is based upon experience and knowledge. . . .

The primitive ancestral form of fishes was almost certainly something rather sharklike, without any true bone in its make-up. From those creatures in a relatively brief period of time evolved a multiplicity of types which are generally divided by scientists into four main groups. These are known as the Placoderms (clumsy "armor-plated fishes"), the Marsipobranchs (jawless, sucking-mouthed fishes), the Selachians (fishes with cartilaginous skeletons), and Pisces (fishes with bony skeletons). Many were experimental forms which found competition too severe and so vanished. All of the first group are extinct. They were too clumsy. There are a few miserable remnants of the Marsipobranchs still alive today (hagfish and lampreys). The Selachii are the sharks and rays which have remained vigorous and numerous, and which are one of the great forces in the waters of the earth. In the vast periods of time since their ancestors first spread terror in prehistoric waters, the sharks have changed perhaps less than any other creatures. Many became extinct, but the line was carried on by forms of vigor and activity. Under Pisces are grouped the vast majority of living fishes, and a number who have vanished, some of great significance in the ancestral line.

The immediate importance of this recent discovery lies in the information it affords us about the developmental processes which have led to the typical forms of fishes, and which have been the subject of much research and speculation. This Coelacanthid specimen (*Latimeria chalumnae*) sheds a great deal of light upon many of those questions, since for some reason parts of this fish are in a

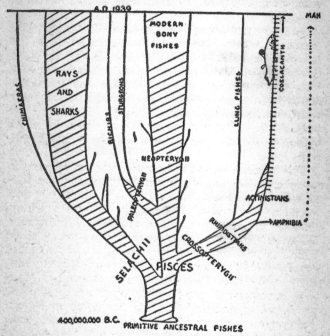

Diagram illustrating the main lines of the evolution of fishes belonging to the groups Selachians and Pisces

condition which may be termed arrested metamorphosis. That is, it bears certain structures which are in process of changing from one thing to another, but the change has not gone to completion. Many of the outer bones of the head in fishes are supposed to have been derived from scales. Also the teeth in the jaws of fishes are believed to be merely scales that have migrated inward and have been changed into tooth-bearing structures. Fins are regarded as having originated from continuous folds of skin developed as stabilizers along the long axis of the body. On these and on many other points the present specimen affords a great deal of important evidence.

The main outline of the evolution of various types belonging to the two chief groups of fishes is shown by the accompanying diagram, which is not to scale. Branches which reach the line 1939 represent groups and forms which have survived to the present day. The others represent extinct forms. The cross-hatched line shows the addition to this scheme necessitated by the recent discovery.

One of the great main branches of the evolutionary tree was the group of the Crossopterygii (or fringe-finned). They were mostly large, active, predaceous fishes that probably dominated the extensive areas in which they occurred. Like most fishes they originated in fresh water and later migrated to the sea. A large number of forms developed, and were characterized by this peculiar "fringe-finned" state, and by the heavy bony armature of the head. Many were not very different from the primitive sharklike ancestor, since their inner skeleton consisted at least partly of cartilage or gristle. They were covered by heavy scales, the outer surface of which was ornamented by an enamel-like substance known as ganoin. Many of them possessed most peculiar tails, known as gephyrocercal, which are really two tails in one, the extreme tip being a remnant of the original true tail which degenerated. Their pectoral and pelvic fins had developed so as to be very like limbs. It had been supposed that the sole living representatives of this ancient line were the few rather scarce species of "lungfishes" living in fresh water in America, Australia and Africa. They are degenerate forms which are but feeble shadows of their active and predaceous ancestors.

After having lived and flourished for some two hundred and fifty million years all those other numerous and vigorous Crossopterygian fishes had been supposed to have become extinct by fifty million years ago. The record in the rocks showed how, after having occurred in great numbers over a wide area, they diminished, until finally all traces ceased before the end of the Mesozoic Era—fifty million years ago. Those important fishes had all vanished. Important because they were a link between the early, intriguing creatures about whose structure we know so little, and the later vertebrates which have given rise finally to man.

The Crossopterygian stock developed principally through a group known as the Rhipidistians. Those flourished from three hundred million years ago for about one hundred million years. Some of those fishes were the ancestral forms which gave rise, almost simultaneously, to three branches of the evolutionary tree: (a) The lungfishes, a thin, feeble line that has survived by living an almost isolated life under conditions that scarcely any other creatures can stand; (b) Actinistian fishes, the Coelacanthidae, a vigorous branch that flourished for a long period and then just petered out long ago (or was thought to have done so); and (c) the amphibia, the origin of all land vertebrates. The two latter groups must have budded off the parent stock very close together. It is not even unlikely that some of the early Coelacanthids made expeditions ashore along with those unknown amphibian ancestors. If that is so, then for some reason they returned to the water and extinction, while the amphibian stock multiplied and throve.

Because of their close connection with the origin of land vertebrates, Crossopterygian fishes have been the subject of most intensive researches. In only a few cases have scientists been able to find anything like complete remains. Mostly there are fragments. In almost all cases the bones of the front part of the snout are missing. There have been found very few clues as to structure other than of the hard parts. All very tantalizing, especially as that "missing link" between fishes and amphibians is still missing.

Now, suddenly, there has appeared this great five-foot fish, bearing the full panoply of his early Mesozoic forebears, but larger than any of them. He is neither puny nor degenerate like the lungfishes, but a great, robust animal prepared and fitted to face all the risks in the sea (except a trawl net!). It is as if a fish of one hundred and fifty million years ago had suddenly come to life. In that incomprehensibly long stretch of time this species has remained virtually unchanged, evidently completely satisfied with itself. In every way this is a true Coelacanthid from that remote past. For at least one hundred and fifty million years this representative of that ancient but vigorous line has lived in such obscurity as never to have left any known traces of its existence.

The discovery of this Coelacanth is a confirmatory link in the chain of evidence upon which the theory of evolution is based. It stands as a high tribute to the reconstructional ability of scientists who have had to work chiefly with distorted and fragmentary remains. Although the scientists engaged in such work have been reasonably confident that their reconstructions were fairly close to the truth, there naturally remained a certain element of doubt. It appeared

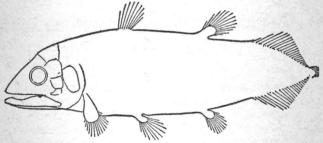

The outline of a Coelacanthid fish, which lived about 150 million years ago, as reconstructed from fossil remains

that there could never be any possibility of comparing their efforts with actual specimens, and many people regarded those reconstructions as mere fantasies. This Coelacanth shows that the scientists, in this case at least, have been remarkably accurate in their reconstructions. . . .

Naturally enough, this fish will fill in many of the gaps in our knowledge of those earlier forms. What is as important is that the discovery makes it at least possible that there may be other primitive creatures, believed long since extinct, lurking unsuspected in the depths of the ocean. It is more than likely that there is a real "sea serpent." So many reliable persons have testified independently to having seen that creature (or those creatures) that it cannot all be fabrication. We know almost nothing about what may be present in the depths of the ocean.

I have been asked where this fish is likely to have lived. My opinion—it can be only a guess—is that the species lived among rocky ledges where trawlers cannot operate, and at depths greater than that at which line fishing is practicable. But a number of factors incline me to believe that it does not live at very great depths. Probably one hundred to two hundred fathoms, along the outer ledges where rocky slopes fade down into the abyss, these Coelacanths lead a "coney-like" existence. Our specimen is probably a stray. We hope that the advent of other specimens will not long be delayed. We may even expect other species.

Pools That Reflect the Past
By John C. Merriam

A diary written on the first Spanish expedition to California contains the description of a peculiar swamp of asphalt or of brea which was reported to flow like melted rock from underneath the earth. In a later stage of exploration the first transcontinental railway survey party found in the same region a locality where mineral pitch poured from the ground in great quantities and sometimes formed large pools or lakes. One spring was pictured as coming from a small opening around which the asphalt spread over a circular space about thirty feet in diameter.

This region of the black springs, known as Rancho La Brea, near the site of present-day Los Angeles, came in time to be operated by the owner as a source of asphaltum used for roofing and paving. Chinese laborers dug the best parts of the deposit from the pools and cleansed it in large vats. The impurities were separated by heating the mass to a temperature at which the liquid asphalt could be poured into molds, leaving a residue consisting of tree stems and bones. The trees were laid aside by the work-men for use as firewood. The bones were thrown on refuse heaps, which came ultimately to contain thousands upon thousands of fragments of skeletons representing many kinds of animals.

Major Hancock, the owner, was familiar with the way

in which all manner of beasts and birds were caught and buried in the brea. He had seen squirrels, chickens, ducks, calves and colts walk unsuspectingly upon the surface of the sticky mass, fall and struggle until they were gradually engulfed. It was a common experience to find cats, dogs and coyotes lured by the struggle of animals thus trapped and themselves become victims of the pool. The considerable losses of fowls and stock from the ranch gave some indication of the extent to which remains of creatures buried in this way might accumulate in the course of years.

It was known to Major Hancock that many of the skeletons found in the pits which he excavated differed greatly from those of barnyard animals and from the coyotes, squirrels and other wild life in the valley. Some of the bones were too large to belong to any creature known to have lived in California, and the skulls of many birds and four-footed animals discovered were entirely different from those of all living things with which he was acquainted.

A naturalist from Boston, who visited Rancho La Brea, was asked to probe the mysteries of the asphalt. He found the innumerable skeletons in the pits to be largely those of animals no longer living anywhere on the earth. A great scimitar-like tooth he described as that of a gigantic cat, similar to remains found only among the relics of ages long preceding historical times.

After the death of the owner, and the stoppage of work on the asphalt deposits, the explanation which the naturalist had given for the presence of bones in the brea seems to have been forgotten. Thirty years later a new series of investigations brought out again the fact that the asphalt pools were the tombs of a vast number of creatures that had inhabited this region at a period probably antedating the present by at least one hundred thousand years. The skeletons buried in the brea were shown to represent not only an immense number of individuals, but a great variety of creatures as well.

Among the animals recognized were such strange forms as the elephant and the camel, together with extinct horses and bison. With these beasts, of which we know similar species living in other parts of the world today, there were mastodons, great ground-living sloths as large as rhinoceroses, gigantic bears differing from every living type, lions exceeding in size all other felines living or extinct, a multitude of cats with knifelike fangs, a huge extinct wolf probably the largest of his tribe, an eaglelike bird greater than the condor, and a multitude of other birds and beasts entirely strange—even to those most deeply learned in the animal life of the present world.

The discoveries at Ranco La Brea told one of the most remarkable known stories of the life of a past period, and naturally led to extended scientific investigations, involving excavation of the asphalt pools and reassembling the skeletons unearthed. The results brought out a vast amount of material, which has been estimated at approximately three million bones.

In this multitude of specimens every detail of structure is retained. The preservation of bones and teeth is not further from perfection than in the remains of recently dead cattle bleaching nearby. Not only is there perfect conservation of the material composing the skeletons, but with this is indubitable evidence of many aspects of use or action in the life of the individual animals represented. Cutting and tearing teeth of wolves and lions are seen worn down where they rubbed upon each other, or against the bones and softer tissues of the creatures upon which they preyed. Molars of bison, camels, horses and elephants are grooved and scored by mastication of their great bulk of vegetable food. There are the bitten and broken bones of many birds, wolves and tigers. In some of these, imperfect contacts led to healing in such manner as to leave crooked or twisted limbs. Abundant specimens show diseased tissues of many parts of the skeleton and teeth. A wolf with a broken foot, and a saber-tooth tiger with fractured and shortened arm tell each a story for which conviction does not depend upon intricate logic or abstruse scientific theory.

One also looks intimately into the changing stages of life of these creatures from babyhood to old age. Lion and tiger cubs and baby wolves show every step in development of skeleton and dentition from the time when the milk teeth just began to appear, on through the many advances to complete replacement by permanent teeth, and into the years of decadence and senility.

Out of early excavations in the pool there came one day the skull of an ancient tiger with sabers broken and shattered to the roots. The ends of these teeth were worn and blunt, as also the front teeth opposing them in the lower jaw. Through long wear produced by biting upon its food in the form of other creatures on which it fed, the fractured blade of one great tooth had been cut down to a smooth broad surface. Also shattered and splintered, the other saber showed less wear on the broken end. This second tooth had maintained itself intact long after the other was broken. But at last it fractured in an unduly heavy or misdirected blow. Instead of carrying death through the swift, sharp strokes of its sabers, the habits of life of this animal were changed, as also in all probability the nature of its food. The tremendous roots of the saber teeth were shrunken, and the bone around them had shriveled. It was an old, emaciated, sunken-cheeked animal that left us this record of its last adventure, in which strength and skill and courage were inadequate.

In the multitude of individuals buried here the vast predominance of types that fed on flesh seems almost beyond belief in contrast to the smaller group of those which formed their prey. But to the flesh-eating animal these pools were continuously baited traps. Any creature captured and struggling in the tar was a lure. The young and inexperienced, the crippled, the incompetent, and the aged ones with failing limbs seem under the stress of hunger to have risked the effort to obtain a meal from prey that lay within their easy reach.

As the centuries passed, like a great procession streaming from surrounding hills and plains, the birds and beasts swept into the blackness of these pools. Here was gathered a multitude of witnesses, who through the "still lapse of ages" waited the time when in the unavoidable evidence of their reality they were to bring a living story of the past before us. They appear today not as formal revelation, but as clear evidence, which through this staying of the hand of destruction permits us to look into the living world of a past eon.

In the great numbers of kinds of beasts and birds entombed in the asphalt pools a large percentage are of types no longer living on any part of the earth. Many of these have their nearest relations in the life of still earlier ages. Such are the saber-tooth, mastodon, ground-sloth and others. The elephant, camel and horse have close relatives living today on other continents. With these two groups are other species, as the coyote and puma, the rodents, many birds, and plants like oak and cypress that have intimate resemblance to species at home in California today. If the whole group of animals and plants from these pools could stand before us, the assemblage would be that of a foreign age or land, but among them would be many friends of our out-of-doors today. Here we face the reality of another world of life shown in many strange phases, and yet the beginning of the present reaches back to overlap that early time.

Search for Early Man
By G. H. R. von Koenigswald

. . . Generally speaking, the preserved remains of prehistoric animals are by no means rare. You can find ancient shells by the millions; the bones of dinosaurs and other reptiles are more precious. But when it comes to the remains of our own ancestors, we have to confess that they are among the greatest rarities. With the exception of Neanderthal man, who is just one step away from us and who lived toward the end of the Ice Age only one hundred thousand years ago, we have had until recently only a few fragmentary bits.

Neanderthal man was forced by the cold climate of the last glacial period to live in caves, and this has made it relatively easy to discover his dwelling places, workshops and burials. But when it comes to the people who lived in the warm interglacial periods or in tropical regions where there were no marked climatic changes, we need a lot of patience, endurance, luck and hard work. It is significant that none of the more important finds in this class have been made by accident. Schoetensack waited twenty years for the Heidelberg jaw, Berckhemer nearly as long for the Steinheim skull. When a human tooth and some other fossils came to light in a Peking drug store in 1900, Davidson

Black had to search the region around Peking most carefully in order to find Chou-kou-tien, the site of Peking man. And all of our finds from Java, which form the subject of this article, are the result of a long and systematic search.

The discovery of early man in Java begins with an *idée fixe*. Eugene Dubois (1858–1940) had just finished his studies in the Netherlands in 1883 when he went to Indonesia, possessed with the idea that he could discover there the oldest remains of man. He was a young man and was very much impressed by Darwin's and Haeckel's ideas on evolution. Lydekker had discovered in the Siwalik fauna of India the upper jaw of an anthropoid ape, which he thought might be an ancient chimpanzee. As the same fauna was known also in Java, Dubois concluded that Java and Sumatra, whose tropical climate had not been influenced by the Ice Age, must be especially favorable places in which to search for the origins of man. He went to the Indies as a medical doctor in the service of the Royal Dutch Army and published his ideas in Batavia. He was lucky enough to arouse the interest of the authorities and, with the full support of the government, was transferred to the Mining Bureau in Batavia to do paleontological research.

He went first to the vicinity of Padang in Sumatra and began, in "European fashion," to excavate in caves. This turned out to be very disappointing. It is commonly believed that caves in the tropics are inhabited by bats, snakes, ghosts, scorpions, evil spirits and lizards, and it would seem that this belief is as old as mankind, for caves have nearly always been avoided by man. The only interesting finds Dubois made there were some teeth of the orang-utan, which is now extinct in Sumatra. This large ape is actually regarded as a kind of man by the Malayans, from whom we get the word "orang-utan," meaning "forest man."

Upon receiving a human skull that had been found in Wadjak, near the southern coast of central Java, Dubois was inspired to go to that locality. There he found the remains of a second specimen. Wadjak man is an extinct primitive type of modern man, perhaps related to the Australian aborigines. Whether he should be regarded as "fossil" is uncertain, for the age of the associated fauna that Dubois collected has never been determined. But from what we know from other localities in Java, these finds cannot be very old and probably should be regarded as only "prehistoric."

From Wadjak, Dubois moved north into the interior of central Java. Large fossil bones, belonging mostly to extinct elephants, had long been known to the natives, who believed they belonged to giants, *raksasas,* the guardians who watch every temple in Bali and ancient Java. Near Madiun, Dubois collected the first fossilized bones of larger mammals, including elephants, hippopotamuses and hyenas, and he also found a very small fragment of a human jaw. He concluded that these remains must be of Pleistocene Age, the geological period popularly known as the Ice Age.

Then, moving west, Dubois discovered a very rich site not far from Ngawi, near Trinil, on the banks of the Solo River. This site could only be worked at low-water level during the dry season. It was here that Dubois, in October, 1891, made his famous discovery—the top of a very low skull with a bony ridge above the eyes. He believed that it belonged to a fossil chimpanzee, the same chimpanzee that Lydekker had described from the Siwalik in India. But in August of the next year he found, only about fifty feet from this find, a complete human thigh bone. It was so human in the characteristics developed for man's erect posture that it could almost have belonged to a modern man. Dubois combined his two finds and in 1894 surprised the world with his famous publication, *"Pithecanthropus erectus,* a Humanlike Transitional Form from Java."

The world was shocked. *Pithecus* means "ape"; *anthropus,* "man"—the "Erect-walking Ape-Man" from Java! Not without purpose had he chosen this name, which had been coined by Haeckel in 1868 for a hypothetical being which should link man with his anthropoid ancestors. Was Dubois' *Pithecanthropus* the "missing link"? No other fossils have ever been discussed by the public with so much vehemence. Man or ape? . . .

The reason for the many different and contradictory opinions is clear; the find (we mean the skull) is too incomplete. The most important part, the region behind the eyes on both sides, is missing, and interpretation of the fragment is indeed difficult.

Dubois tried to find more material that might solve the question, but without success. Nor did the German Selenka Expedition, which worked in Trinil in 1907–1908, find anything belonging to *Pithecanthropus*. However, they published a description of the animal remains from this geological horizon, which filled a great gap in our knowledge. It proved that this fauna, which Dubois had tried to make Pliocene (from one to seven million years old), could not be older than Pleistocene (a million years old at the most).

In 1929, news came from China that Davidson Black had succeeded in finding the skull of Peking man. And Peking man was really a man, not only from the anatomical point of view, but because he already knew the use of stone implements and fire. In describing the skull, Black found that it resembled the skull of *Pithecanthropus* in so many features as to indicate a close relationship between the two. So by analogy it became clear that our Java ape-man was a human being, in spite of his primitiveness.

Curiously enough, now that everyone else was convinced, Dubois changed his opinion completely. Basing his new ideas only on very theoretical speculations, he now regarded his *Pithecanthropus* as a gigantic gibbon, denying every relationship with Peking man.

It seemed that the only way to convince Dubois would be to find a more complete *Pithecanthropus* skull in Java. An opportunity came when the Geological Survey of the Netherlands East Indies was established and began the systematic geological mapping of that region. In 1930 I went to Java to join the Survey as a paleontologist. Our headquarters were at Bandung, a beautiful town in the mountains of western Java. From the first moment, I hoped for a chance to solve the puzzle of *Pithecanthropus*.

We gradually collected enough specimens to learn that the animal life of Java had not been as uniform as Dubois had led us to believe, and that with the help of certain guide fossils, it was possible to classify rock formations that were otherwise quite similar. A correlation with the formations in India could be worked out, and we could prove that Trinil was not quite as old as Dubois had suggested. At least three horizons of Pleistocene Age were represented. We showed that Trinil was of middle Pleistocene Age, which means that *Pithecanthropus* lived about three hundred thousand years ago.

It was shortly after my arrival in Java in September, 1931, that my colleague, the late C. Ter Haar, discovered a high-level river terrace on the Solo River north of Ngawi, at Ngandong. He brought back quite a collection of fossil bones, and this encouraged the Survey to start excavations immediately. Among the first specimens sent to Bandung were, to our great surprise, fragments of two human skulls with low, receding foreheads. They were more primitive than modern man but more advanced than *Pithecanthropus,* and they represented a type which might be classified as neanderthaloid. From the geological point of view also, this so-called "Solo man" was younger than Trinil man. . . .

My first personal encounter with early man came on a hot day in June, 1937. A report had come that our workers in Ngandong had found what might be a human skull. They had left the find untouched and were waiting for assistance. So we went out—slim, always good-humored Ter Haar and I. We went by train to Ngawi and then set out on foot for the Solo River, followed by a whole caravan of coolies carrying our baggage on bamboo poles on their bare shoulders. It was about six miles to the site. We passed through the dense teakwood forest of the Kendeng Hills, and then, quite suddenly, we were standing on the bank of the Solo River. Our excavation was almost within the small hamlet of Ngandong, which consisted of only a few bamboo huts. Sixty feet or so above the river, spared from erosion, was a very limited remnant of a gravel deposit, only about one to three yards thick. From this came all our bones.

Our collectors had covered the precious find with sand for protection. We carefully began to remove the earth. Then, suddenly, there came to light the object we had expected but were thrilled to see—the upper part of a human skull! It lay upside down in the gravel, partly covered by a cemented crust of sand. I was so excited that I overexposed all of my pictures! It was skull No. VI, finest specimen in the whole series of Solo skulls.

For *Pithecanthropus* himself we had to wait longer. In

1936 my colleague Duyfjes, a very able young geologist who died in a prison camp during the war, had one of our native collectors working near Modjokerto, west of Surabaya. Here this man discovered a small accumulation of fossil bones. Digging only about a yard deep, he found a curious human skull, very small and with very thin bones. It was the fossilized skull of a baby. A direct comparison with Dubois' find was impossible, but the skull came from a deeper level, known to be older than the layer where his was found. We called the baby *"Homo" modjokertensis* and suggested that it might belong to *Pithecanthropus*. We had, for the first time, proved the existence of human beings in the lower Pleistocene of Java. But we could not convince Dubois, either by this find or by a fine fragment of a lower jaw (*Pithecanthropus* B), which closely resembled the lower jaw of Peking man. This latter had been found by my collectors in 1936, but it only came to my attention in 1937 after my return from America. . . .

From the outset of my work in Java, I had also begun to make a collection of the teeth of extinct mammals from China. These teeth are sold also outside of China—even in New York—by the Chinese drug stores as "dragon teeth," and they are considered a special and very powerful medicine. By visiting one drug store after another in Java, it was fairly easy to collect teeth of rhinoceroses, *Hipparion* (a three-toed horse), a large giraffe, and other mammals of the Tertiary Era. They are heavily mineralized, and often damaged on purpose to show the small calcite crystals in the pulp cavities. . . .

Among these isolated teeth from China there were three large molars (I discovered a fourth one in 1939) that belong to the largest higher primate ever found, much larger than any gorilla. I described them as a new species, *Gigantopithecus blacki,* meaning "the gigantic ape of Black," named after Davidson Black, the discoverer of Peking man. From the beginning, some of the characteristics of these teeth, known only in human teeth, puzzled me. It was not until many years later that new finds in Java helped us to interpret them. . . .

I had two Indonesian chief collectors, for whose help and loyalty I am greatly indebted, and under them there were hundreds of natives to aid in the search. Every fragment of a fossil that they found was bought. We paid premiums for important finds and stimulated interest by means of festivals with *gamelang* and *rongengs*—native orchestra and dancing girls. We paid good collectors in advance and sent sick children to hospitals. Most of the material obtained was worthless and had to be thrown away, but we had to encourage collectors. We had to buy everything because if a man found three pig teeth, he would not look for more until these were bought. So we had to spend quite a lot of money for nothing (some people certainly regarded me as a fool), but it seemed the only way to get results.

And results came! Only a few months after my return to Java, my man sent me a fragment that was unmistakably part of an ancient human skull. I went directly out to the collecting fields. There, on the banks of a small river, nearly dry at that season, lay the fragments of a skull, washed out of the sandstones and conglomerates that contained the Trinil fauna. With a whole bunch of excited natives, we crept up the hillside, collecting every bone fragment we could discover. I had promised the sum of ten cents for every fragment belonging to that human skull. But I had underestimated the "big business" ability of my brown collectors. The result was terrible! Behind my back they broke the larger fragments into pieces in order to increase the number of sales!

We collected about forty fragments of which thirty belonged to the skull. They were very thick, averaging about one centimeter (.39 inch), and could easily be fitted together. They formed a fine, nearly complete *Pithecanthropus* skullcap. Now, at last, we had him!

It would be difficult to find, without careful selection, two modern skulls that resembled each other as much in detail as did the Trinil find and this new skull—except that the latter is more complete. This time, the important side parts were preserved on both sides, and now we could prove beyond doubt that *Pithecanthropus* belonged to the human family.

I immediately informed Professor Dubois, who was living in Haarlem. His attitude was very disappointing. He published the photograph of my find, which I had sent him only for personal information, and he tried to prove by misleading measurements that the new skull—which belonged, as he had to admit, to a human being—was more or less a fake. According to him, my find belonged to a young representative of Solo man, while his *Pithecanthropus* had to remain an ape. He made any collaboration between us impossible and refused to acknowledge that a single one of the new finds belonged to *Pithecanthropus*. During the German occupation of the Netherlands, only a few weeks before his death, he still published a very confused article, the last of a whole series on this subject.

Davidson Black had suggested a relationship between Peking man and *Pithecanthropus*. To study this problem further, I was invited by his successor, Professor Franz Weidenreich, to bring my specimens to the Rockefeller Institute in Peking for comparison. The Geological Survey agreed. Our studies there, in 1939, proved that Davidson Black had been right. The resemblance between these two early human types was even greater than we had formerly believed. We were also able to demonstrate that Dubois' interpretation of his own find was wrong. The thick piece of bone that he had thought to be part of the ear was actually only the remnant of a thick bony ridge. X-ray pictures of the new skull revealed sutures not visible on the surface which proved that my reconstruction was correct.

But *Pithecanthropus* II was not the only find. In 1938 came No. III, from a new site not far from the locality that yielded No. II, and certainly from the same level. It is only a small fragment, consisting of the back of a juvenile skull. And in 1939 we found *Pithecanthropus* IV, the back part and upper jaw of a crushed skull, and this specimen came from the lower level. The barren hillside where this find came to light seems dull and uninteresting. But this is a very important specimen, enabling us for the first time to make a trustworthy reconstruction of the entire skull. This skull is larger and heavier than either II or III, and has been called *Pithecanthropus robustus* by Dr. Weidenreich.

Early in 1941 one of our collectors sent us part of an enormous human jaw, which had likewise been found in the lower horizon. For years I had kept some large, isolated teeth which I felt could not belong to an orang-utan; but human teeth of this size seemed against all theory. Now, however, we had a jaw that surpassed a gorilla's in size, yet showed unmistakable human characteristics. I carried the fragment in my pocket for days to get accustomed to the idea! We had discovered a giant, which we named *Meganthropus paleojavanicus* (meaning "great," *anthropus,* "man"). It was only one step further to recognize the enormous teeth from China as human. . . .

These new finds, the oldest remains of man yet discovered, are surely about five hundred thousand years old. They show us a new aspect of human evolution, for they indicate that man's ancestors were giants and that we reached our present physical proportions through a decrease in the size of our jaws and teeth—a conclusion wholly unsuspected until now. Much work must be done before we can come to definite conclusions. . . .

The Future of Man as an Inhabitant of the Earth

By Kirtley Mather

During the first decade or two of the current century, geologists, astronomers and physicists engaged in many discussions concerning the future of the earth as an abode for life. Some believed that "the end of the world" was relatively close at hand; others, that the prospect for the future was to be measured in terms of hundreds of thousands if not of millions of years. As usual in scientific circles, there has emerged from the conflict of ideas during the years of discussion a general unanimity of opinion, and today the geologic outlook for the future of the earth is quite clear.

Since the turn of the century . . . innumerable details of earth history have been deciphered to give a trustworthy record of the changes that the earth and its inhabitants have undergone in the past. The key to unlock the secrets of the future is now available in this knowledge of the past, and with our present understanding of the processes of nature that key may be intelligently used. All the geologic evidence combines to lead us unmistakably to the conclusion that for many scores, if not for hundreds of millions of years to come, the earth will continue to be a comfortably habitable abode for creatures like ourselves.

Surface temperatures of the earth, the most important item in any consideration of its long-range habitability, are determined by the receipt of solar energy distributed through atmospheric agencies. . . . The nineteenth-century picture of the earth, initially fiery hot but progressively cooling so that yesterday it displayed a glacial climate and tomorrow it will be too frigid to support life, may now be thrown into the discard. The earth will "grow old and die" only as a result of failure to receive adequate supplies of radiant energy from the sun. The prospect that the sun will "burn itself out" in a decrepit old age is so remote as to baffle all attempts to date that untoward event even by those who are expert in manipulating astronomic figures. Nor is there any likelihood that the space relations between earth and sun will change appreciably within scores of millions of years and put the earth either too close to the sun or too distant from it for comfort.

The lurid pictures of a sudden catastrophic debacle resulting from collision with some other heavenly body—comet, planet, star or what you will—are products of a vivid imagination wholly without foundation in astronomic fact or theory.

The only plausible alternative to the conclusion that earth and sun will continue the even tenor of their ways for an inconceivably long period of time is that the sun will some day imitate the supernovae occasionally detected among the stars and terminate the existence of the entire solar system by a gigantic explosion. Precisely one such supernova has been observed within the galaxy of the Milky Way and several such in all the other galaxies of stars during the past few decades. The astronomers could, therefore, calculate for us the chances on a statistical basis that any individual star—the sun, for example—would suffer such a fate within any given period of time. The result would be a figure so infinitesimal as to set at rest the mind of even the most jittery of questioners. . . .

The geologist may, therefore, turn with confidence from

the long perspective of geologic past with its one and a half to two billion years of recorded earth history to a similarly long prospect for the future. Time is one of the most overwhelming resources of our universe.

It should not be inferred, however, that the earth will continue in the future to display the same environmental conditions as those which we enjoy today. The history of mankind thus far has been enacted against a background that in the full perspective of earth history is truly extraordinary. The geologic period in which we live is a time of unusually rugged and extensive lands, with notably varied climate ranging from the glacial cold of Greenland and Antarctica to the oppressive warmth and humidity of certain equatorial regions. . . . The probability is strong that eventually, say in five or ten million years, the earth will display again the physical conditions of many past geologic periods that were characterized by broad, low lands, wide, shallow seas and uniform, genial climate.

But most of us have a greater interest in the next few centuries than in the subsequent millions of years. Minor changes in climate will doubtless occur just as they have in the last few thousand years. Unfortunately, or perhaps fortunately, there is no basis for prediction concerning their nature, whether for better or for worse. There is really no good reason for referring to the present as "a post-glacial epoch"; it may prove to be an interglacial epoch. But our ancestors weathered ice ages in the past, and presumably we are better equipped for such contingencies than they were. Should the average annual temperature of the earth as a whole be reduced something like 10° F. and remain at that lower level for a few millennia, it is likely that once more the greater part of Canada, the northern United States and the Scandinavian countries would be buried beneath great ice sheets. But in consequence of the removal of water from the sea as vapor to form the snow to produce the glacial ice, considerable areas now shallowly submerged along the coastlines in middle and equatorial latitudes would emerge as dry land. Indeed, it is likely that the area of land suitable for human abode would be nearly or quite as great at the climax of a glacial period as it is today.

By the same token, the disappearance of existing bodies of glacial ice as a result of rapid amelioration of climate in the not distant future would, if it occurred, be a decidedly mixed blessing. Return to the sea the water now imprisoned in the ice on the Arctic islands, Greenland and Antarctica without any compensating changes in crustal elevation, and sea level would be raised one hundred fifty to one hundred sixty feet in the world around. Considering the number of people who now work or sleep in buildings in metropolitan communities not over one hundred fifty feet above sea level, the importance of such a change is readily apparent. But from the geologists' point of view these are relatively trivial matters. With due deference to the nature of the climatic variations and geologic changes which are certain to occur in the next few thousand years, there is nothing to be expected from such sources that would seriously deter the human species from maintaining a comfortable existence on the surface of the earth for an indefinitely long period of time—a period to be measured in millions rather than in mere thousands of years. . . .

From the point of view attained through knowledge of geologic life development, man has today a unique opportunity to gain continuing security for himself and his progeny on the face of the earth, but whether or not he takes advantage of that opportunity is to be determined largely by himself. So far as we can tell, man is the first animal possessing the power to determine his own evolutionary destiny, but there is nothing in the record which guarantees that he will use that power wisely.

The animal species that in the past have been able to maintain their existence for more than two or three million years are relatively few in number. Most of them were comparatively simple types belonging to the less highly organized branches or phyla of the animal kingdom. Many were inhabitants of the sea where environmental conditions were remarkably stable throughout long periods of time. Among placental mammals, the major subdivision of the vertebrates to which man belongs, there is no similar record of longevity. Except under extraordinary conditions of geographic isolation, no species of placental mammal has persisted more than two or three million years. No matter how successful it may have been temporarily in multiplying and spreading over the face of the earth, each has become extinct in a geologically brief span of time. Perhaps a half-million years might appropriately be taken as the average "life" of a species in this group of highly organized and notably complex creatures.

But extinction does not necessarily mean failure; it has frequently indicated the acme of achievement. For example, some of the now extinct three-toed horses and four-toed camels passed on "the torch of progress" to their descendants, the one-toed horses and two-toed camels, and thus gained long continuing security for their kind.

What then does the future hold for mankind? Genus *Homo* has already existed for three or four hundred thousand years; the species *Homo sapiens* has about fifty thousand years to its credit. If the average applies, we may expect nearly or quite a half-million years more of existence for our kind and then either oblivion as we reach the end of a blind alley or progressive development into some type of descendant better adjusted than we to the total environmental factors of the time.

But does the average apply? Must man exit from the scene through either of the doors, that which closed behind the dinosaurs and titanotheres or that which opened before the three-toed horses and notharctines?

Most creatures have gained security by specializing in adjustment of structure and habit to particular environmental conditions, whereas man is a specialist in adjustability of structures and habits to a variety of environments. No other vertebrate can live as can he on Antarctic Ice Cap, in Amazonian jungle, beneath the surface of the sea or high in the air.

Furthermore, man is the world's foremost specialist in transforming environments to bring them within the range of his powers. Far more efficient than the beaver or the mound-building ant, he drains the swamp, irrigates the desert, tunnels the mountain, bridges the river, digs the canal, conditions the air in home, factory and office.

As a matter of fact, adjustability to environment is accomplished more by controlling surroundings than by modifying internal organs or essential functions of the body. When we ascend with Major Stevens into the stratosphere, or dive with Dr. Beebe five hundred fathoms deep off Bermuda, or live with Admiral Byrd through the long night of Little America, we take along with us a sample of sea-level atmosphere and temperate climate that is our real environment in a situation otherwise unbearable. Fur-lined parkas and tropical linen suits are but a medium for insuring an immediate environment as nearly as possible like that of middle latitudes when living in polar or equatorial surroundings.

But regardless of interpretation of procedure, the result is clear. Man has placed himself in control of external conditions to an extent immeasurably greater than any other creature. He has practically "drawn the teeth" of environment.

Although we know little of the details, it is certain that most of the creatures of the past, who "have had their day and ceased to be," were forced into extinction by changes of one sort or another in their environment, changes which came with such relative speed that they were unable to make adjustment to them in time. Man need have no fear on that score.

It is, however, immediately apparent that man's conquest of his surroundings has resulted from his clever use of things. Unless there is a ceaseless flow of cotton, flax and wool, of iron, coal and petroleum, of copper, lead and tin, from ground to processing plant to consumer, he becomes a puny weakling. It is because he uses certain resources provided by his environment that he is freed from slavery to his environment. Are these resources adequate to keep him supplied with what he needs to maintain indefinitely the sort of existence to which he has accustomed himself?

There are two fundamental sources of the goods and the energy that man uses in the grim business of obtaining the sort of living that he apparently desires. On the one hand there is the farm and the waterfall, on the other there is the mine and the quarry. Things which grow in the field or forest and power produced by falling water are in the category of annual income. Now that scientific research has made available the limitless quantity of nitrogen in the air for use as fertilizer, the resources of the plant and animal kingdoms are renewable; we use them, but we need never use them up. In startling contrast, the resources of the mineral kingdom are nonrenewable; they are in the category of accumulated capital. Petroleum and coal, copper and iron, lead and vanadium, these and many other prerequisites of modern civilization have been accumulated by Nature through hundreds of millions of years of geologic activity. Thanks to scientific research, man is exhausting that store of mineral wealth in a few hundred, or at most a few thousand, years. That inescapable fact is at rock bottom one of the most fundamental causes of economic distress, of war between nations and of strife between classes. . . .

Data are not nearly so precise for the majority of foreign countries as for the United States. It is, however, fairly safe to conclude that the world stores of petroleum will last only something like seventy-five years at the present rate of withdrawal. With the possible exception of Mexico, no other country has been as successful as the United States in the attempt to exhaust its petroleum resources in the shortest possible period of time, but rapid progress toward that result is now being made in many regions.

Lest we become too pessimistic in response to such unwelcome figures, we should promptly note that substitutes for petroleum are already known. Gasoline, fuel oil and lubricating oil can now be manufactured from coal and other rocks rich in carbon by processes of hydrogenation and polymerization. These are expensive processes and their products cannot now compete with the products from petroleum even in countries far removed, both geographically and psychologically, from the more productive oil fields. They will, however, come into use more and more in the next few decades.

Enough bituminous and sub-bituminous coal is known to be available within the United States to meet the present annual demand for coal, plus enough to manufacture gasoline and fuel oil in sufficient quantity to meet current demands for at least two thousand years. In addition there is enough oil shale—a rock rich in carbon but containing little or no oil—to meet the present needs for petroleum products for at least three thousand or four thousand years.

Although petroleum affords an excellent illustration of the relation of nonrenewable resources to the activities of man, it is by no means typical of the items comprising

Nature's accumulated capital. For nearly all of the important nonrenewable resources, the known world stores are thousands of times as great as the annual world consumption instead of less than a hundred times. But for the few which, like petroleum, are not known to be available in such vast quantities, the story is much the same. Substitutes are already known, or potential sources of alternative supply are already at hand, in quantities adequate to meet our current needs for at least two thousand or three thousand years. There is, therefore, no prospect of the imminent exhaustion of any of the essential raw materials, so far as the world as a whole is concerned, provided our demands for them are not multiplied rapidly in the future. . . .

However, current consumption of nonrenewable resources cannot be taken as the basis for computing the "life" of such stores of basic materials. The demand for automobiles, telephones, radios, airplanes and zippers is today very unevenly distributed. Only a small fraction of the human population uses such things in any large amounts. Other peoples are beginning to demand them and will do so increasingly as they become acquainted with the "benefits of civilization." In a few decades, unless we return to savagery, the world demand for many nonrenewable resources will be twice or thrice that of today.

Taking all these things into consideration, it would appear that world stores of needed natural resources are adequate to supply a basis for the comfortable existence of every human being who is likely to dwell anywhere on the face of the earth for something like a thousand years to come. . . .

One hundred years ago, something like 80 per cent of all the things man used had their source on farms; most of the energy used to do the work of the world came from the muscles of living beings and from falling water. Today only about 30 per cent of the things man uses come from things that grow; most of the energy with which work is done comes from petroleum and coal. For a century or more, the policy has been to use relatively less of the annual income and more of the stored capital.

Now comes the change. Automobile steering wheels are made from soy beans; piano keys from cottage cheese; innumerable articles fashioned of plastics are produced in part from corncobs and alfalfa; multitudinous metal and rubber substitutes are synthesized from various farm crops. Energy is transmitted at high voltages for hundreds of miles from hydroelectric turbines. A considerable portion of the annual budget for research is being devoted to progress in the direction of using more of the renewable resources—man's annual income, and less of the nonrenewable resources—nature's stored capital.

What this new policy will mean is readily apparent. With progress along such lines, the pressure for political control of metalliferous ore deposits, coal fields and oil pools is lessened. Much of the physical basis for international jealousy is liquidated. At last the intelligence of science may make it truly practical to beat our "swords into ploughshares," our "spears into pruning hooks."

Again comes the insistent question from the pessimistic critic. Is there land enough? Is there sufficient fertile soil to provide adequate food and in addition the plant materials for the ever expanding chemical industries? And again we hear the same reply. Yes, there is enough and to spare. J. D. Bernal computes from apparently valid data that the cultivation of two billion acres of land by the methods now in vogue in Great Britain would provide an optimum food supply for the entire population of the earth. "Two billion acres is less than half the present cultivated area of four billion two hundred million acres, itself hardly 12 per cent of the land surface of the earth." And in this calculation no account is taken of the increased yields that may confidently be expected from the continuing research of agronomists, plant breeders and experts in animal husbandry, not to mention recent developments in the new science of the soilless growth of plants. Evidently, the predictions of Malthus notwithstanding, mankind need have no fear that increasing populations will place an impossible burden upon the available sources of food. Human ingenuity, intelligent use of renewable resources, wise adjustment of structures and habits to environmental conditions seem competent to dispel that dread shadow.

But these optimistic conclusions concerning the relation of man to the nonrenewable and renewable resources essential for comfortable existence are based upon world statistics. Obviously they do not apply with equal force to the economy of individual nations. No nation, not even the Soviet Union, Brazil or the United States of America, embraces within its political frontiers a sufficient variety of geologic structures to give it adequate supplies of all the various metalliferous ores necessary as raw materials for modern industrial operations. The United States, for example, must import nickel, tin, antimony, chromium and platinum if American maufacturers are to use those metals in the fabrication of articles essential to what we are pleased to call the civilized way of life. Likewise, no nation enjoys a sufficient variety of climatic conditions to permit all kinds of foodstuffs to be grown on its farms and fields or gathered from its forests, and to allow the growth of all the various plants contributing raw materials to industry. The United States, again the most significant example for us, is forced to import all the bananas, coffee, tea, camphor, coconuts, flax, jute, quinine, rubber and shellac consumed in this country, either from foreign countries or its own overseas possessions. It is entirely possible that, within a few decades, substitutes of domestic origin may be available to take the place of many, or even all, of such commodities or that plant breeding and agronomists may find a practical way of extending the geographical limits of some of the plants whose products are considered essential so that any nation occupying a large fraction of any continent may actually be self-sufficient. But for the present and probably for a long time to come it is evident that every nation is dependent upon many other nations for the raw materials that it needs for its own industrial prosperity.

Perhaps the most important fact concerning the life of man today is this fact of interdependence. No nation, community or individual can gain any lasting measure of security without taking that fact into consideration. The resources that man must utilize, if he wishes to escape the fate of his less intelligent relatives now known only by their fossil remains, are unevenly distributed and locally concentrated. The techniques of discovering and utilizing them are now fairly well known, but satisfactory procedures for making them and their products available to all members of the human family are not close at hand.

The very solution of the physical problems which man encounters in his attempt to maintain his foothold upon the earth brings him all the more forcefully into bruising contact with physical and spiritual problems that must also be solved if he is to continue his existence on this planet. The critical question for the twentieth century is: How can two or three billion human beings be satisfactorily organized for the wise use and equitable distribution of resources that are abundant enough for all, but are unevenly scattered over the face of the earth? Clearly, the future of man depends upon finding and applying the correct answer to that specific but far-reaching question.

Man is not only a specialist in the art of co-ordinated activity, but the trend toward organization is recognizable in the entire development of cosmic administration. Electrons, neutrons and protons are organized into atoms, atoms into molecules, molecules into compounds. Some of the compounds prove to be cells, and these are organized to form individual plants and animals. Latest of all in the history of creative evolution certain individuals have been organized into societies. Transcending all that has gone before is the development of human society, obviously the most difficult, but at the same time potentially the most glorious organization yet attempted.

Two antagonistic alternatives present themselves as possible bases for this organization. The issue between the two has never before been so clearly drawn as it is today. The social group, whether it be the family, the industrial or commercial company, or the political unit, may be organized on the principle of regimentation, or it may be developed according to democratic principles. Both methods are being tried under a variety of conditions, and each has something to be said in its favor. But both cannot be equally conducive to the continuing existence of mankind. One or the other must be selected as the basis for the future security of man.

If regimentation be the choice, then the great mass of humankind must be trained for obedience—blind, unquestioning, but superbly skillful obedience. The educator becomes the intellectual and spiritual counterpart of the drill sergeant in the army. This is no menial task, nor is its objective a mean one. Skill is a commodity of which there is never likely to be an oversupply. On the other hand, if democracy be the choice, the great mass of humankind must be trained for wise, self-determined co-operation. Precisely those qualities of mind and heart which have long been extolled in Christian doctrine must be developed to the fullest possible extent. Not only skill but also the ability to govern oneself, the eternal prerequisite for freedom, must be developed in each member of the group.

Insofar as physical existence is concerned, there would seem to be little or no choice between these alternatives. Human nature being what it is today, perhaps the regimentation of society may temporarily be the more efficient method. But the full circle of organic law embraces more than mere existence. From the continuity of the evolutionary process there has emerged a creature who is aware of vivid values in life that may be found beyond the goods necessary for comfortable existence. Ideas and ideals are powerful determining factors in the world today, and among them the ideal of freedom for the individual in the midst of social restraint is the most vital and compelling of all. Though it baffle our scientific tools for measurement, it is nonetheless a reality.

It is in the yearning for freedom, the love of beauty, the search for truth, the recognition of moral law and in the awareness of spiritual forces that human nature is distinguished from all other sorts of nature. Man shares with other animals the need for satisfactory economics, for adequate food and shelter, for the goods essential to existence, but his needs transcend these physical factors because his nature differs from theirs. Probably nine-tenths of all the words that have been used since the dawn of speech in reference to "human nature" have referred to those elements in the nature of man that are shared with other animals rather than to those that are man's unique possession. It would be far better to concentrate upon the latter and thus to distinguish human nature from animal nature.

Regimentation may be good for man as an animal; through that type of social organization his need for goods may be efficiently supplied. But regimentation is certainly not good for human nature as thus distinguished. Experience verifies what wisdom foresees; regimentation stultifies the spirit, destroys personality, standardizes thought and action. Worst of all, regimentation means stagnation of the creative process and, as we have seen, stagnation among the more complexly organized vertebrates has led inevitably to extinction. If man attempts to live by bread alone, mankind commits collective suicide. Apparently the best and perhaps the only chance for mankind to succeed in the quest for security is through progress in the art of living on a high spiritual plane rather than through exclusive attention to the science of existence on a purely physical level.

To put this same thought in more specific terms, it means that co-ordinated activity directed toward efficient organization of individuals must become co-operative activity directed toward the enrichment of personality within an efficiently organized society. This requires both intelligence and good will.

Fortunately, these characteristics are uniquely developed in the species of placental mammal with which we are pre-eminently concerned. Man is a specialist in the use of both. The trend of the past five thousand years may well continue, despite numerous temporary setbacks, throughout the next few centuries at least.

It is sometimes suggested that because man has specialized in brains, brains may cause his downfall, just as presumably the overspecialization in external armament contributed to the downfall of certain herbivorous dinosaurs. That argument by analogy is, however, heavily punctuated with fallacies. There is as yet no evidence that mankind is weighted down with a superabundance of intelligence. On the contrary, it is failure to act intelligently that endangers individuals and groups in the midst of competition. To see in advance the remote consequences of contemplated action is an ability that ought to be increasingly cultivated rather than scouted as a menace.

There seems to be no good reason why a sound mind should not be accompanied by a sound body. If the number of psychopathic individuals is increasing in this high-speed, technologic age, it is a challenge to be met not by bemoaning the imminent collapse of civilization but by intelligent adjustment of habits and activities to the new demands of the new times.

Once the commitment is made to the belief that the co-operative way of life offers the best chance for the future security of man as an inhabitant of the earth, the need is greater for intelligence to be used as a guide for good will, rather than for good will to be applied as a brake on any possible increase in intelligence.

The roots of self-centered individualism may be traced backward for at least six hundred million years in the record of geologic life development, whereas our heritage of social consciousness dates from a time only about sixty million years ago when gregarious instincts became clearly evident among placental mammals. That trend is, however, especially apparent in the group from which mankind has stemmed.

Man is still in the stage of specific youth. His golden age, if any, is in the future rather than in the past. Human nature is still sufficiently plastic and pliable to permit considerable change, notably in this important area of attitudes and relationships wherein the increase of good will as a motive for action seems most likely to result in beneficial adjustments to the new factors in the environment.

In thus seeking a satisfactory co-ordination of intelligence and good will, it becomes necessary for research scientists to give more thought than has been customary in the past to the social consequences of their work. They share with statesmen, politicians, educators and all molders of public opinion the responsibility for determining the uses to which the new tools provided by scientific research are put. As scientists, they should continue to seek truth regardless of its consequences and to increase human efficiency in every possible way, but as members of society, as individual representatives of a species seeking future security as inhabitants of the earth, they must also do their utmost to ensure wise use of knowledge and constructive application of energy.

There is a real difference between the so-called social sciences and the natural and physical sciences that has an important bearing here. It is not that there is anything unnatural about the social sciences. Man is a part of nature, and the study of human society is just as truly natural science in the real sense of the term as any other study. The difference arises from the peculiar factors and particular functions pertaining to the co-operative way of life. Whereas the scientific use of things may be achieved through the efforts of a very small minority of the citizens, provided with adequate facilities for research, the scientific organization of society in a democracy can be achieved only when the majority of its citizens have the scientific attitude toward social problems and act in accordance with that attitude of mind. In other words, only a few physicists, chemists and technologists are required for the mastery of our physical environment, but for victory in the struggle with ourselves every man must be his own sociologist.

Although this places upon the forces of education a Herculean task, it is not nearly so impossible an assignment as at a first glance it might appear to be. In the first place, the responsibility upon the individual citizen is rarely that of designing a new social structure or charting a new program for society. Almost invariably it is his duty merely to select from many plans, programs or proposals the one that seems to him most likely to produce the most desirable results for all concerned. In the second place, scientific habits of mind have already been developed to a greater extent than is ordinarily recognized. The garage mechanic attacks the problem of a balky automobile in a truly scientific manner. The salesman uses psychology in planning his approach to a difficult prospect. The housewife thinks scientifically when about to concoct a new dessert or redecorate the living room. In most cases, it is only necessary to apply in the area of social relationships the same habits of mind that have been followed in the area of individual behavior.

In conclusion, the outlook for the future of man as an inhabitant of the earth is far from pessimistic. If certain tendencies already developing are encouraged and certain resources already available are capitalized to the full, there is good reason to expect that mankind will maintain existence and even live happily for an indefinitely long period of time. The opportunity is his to demonstrate the intrinsic worth of biologic phenomena and thus to justify the vast expenditure of time and energy involved in organic evolution. With greater emphasis upon the development of intelligence and good will, he may achieve that which the temporarily triumphant dynasties of the past have failed to achieve. Thus the geologist may turn from the long perspective of geologic history to the enticing vista of the geologic future of earth and man with high hope and even with confident assurance.

INDEX